THE MENSA® BOOK OF PUZZLE CHALLENGES

FAMILY LEARNING

FAMILY LEARNING

A DK PUBLISHING BOOK

Produced for DK Publishing by Carlton Books Ltd.,
20 St Anne's Court, Wardour Street, London W1V 3AW
Project Manager: Julian Flanders
Design Manager: Paul Messam
Project Editor: Tim Dedopulos
Production: Alexia Turner

For Dorling Kindersley
Managing Editor: Jayne Parsons
Managing Art Editor: Gill Shaw
Jacket Design: Mark Richards

First American Edition, 1998
10 9 8 7 6 5 4 3 2
Published in the United States by DK Publishing Inc., New
York, New York 10016

ISBN 0 7894 3559 4

Color reproductions by Lydia Litho, London
Printed and bound in Italy

Contents

MENSA MEMBERSHIP

When you've finished the puzzles in this book, you might like to join Mensa, the international society for people who are good at solving difficult problems. For details and your membership test write to your national Mensa organization.

American Mensa can be contacted at:
>American Mensa Limited
>201 Main Street Suite 1101
>Fort Worth, TX 76102

Alternatively, for details of the other national Mensa organisations, contact:
>Mensa International Limited
>15 The Ivories
>628 Northampton Street
>London N1 2NY
>England

They will be happy to put you in touch with your own national Mensa.

This book has been divided up into three sections: Word Puzzles, Number Puzzles, and Code Puzzles. Within each section, there are puzzles graded Easy, Difficult, and Very Tough. The puzzles have been numbered randomly with numbers between 1 and 200, to make sure that you don't accidentally see the answer to the next puzzle.

The three different types of puzzles each have their own special symbol. These are:

◆ Word Puzzles　　★ Number Puzzles　　○ Code Puzzles

These symbols will show you what type of puzzle the question or answer belongs to.

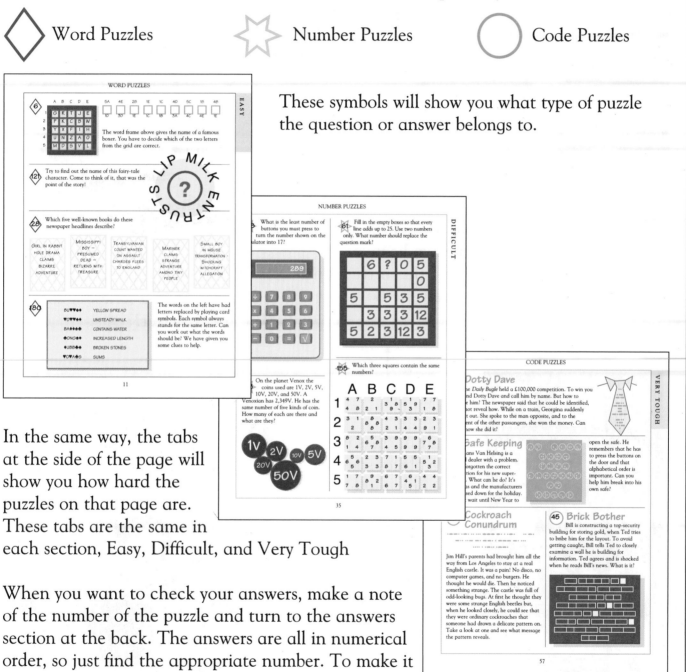

In the same way, the tabs at the side of the page will show you how hard the puzzles on that page are. These tabs are the same in each section, Easy, Difficult, and Very Tough

When you want to check your answers, make a note of the number of the puzzle and turn to the answers section at the back. The answers are all in numerical order, so just find the appropriate number. To make it simple for you, each answer is marked with the symbol for its puzzle type. Remember not to read the other answers, though! Good luck and happy puzzling.

EASY

151 Replace each question mark with a letter to form a word. Read down; the missing letters should spell the names of five things found in a kitchen. What are they?

JU	M?	BO
GR	I?	ND
PA	C?	ED
AR	R?	AY
AB	O?	VE
MO	V?	ED
CR	A?	CK
RI	V?	ET
FR	E?	AK

HI	?	ER
AM	?	ND
OU	?	ER
EX	?	RA
SA	?	TY
ST	?	RN

HU	?	KY
CR	?	NE
AC	?	TE
OS	?	AR
TH	?	ME
VE	?	GE

OF	F?	ER
DI	R?	TY
RA	I?	NY
WE	D?	GE
AN	G?	ER
KN	E?	AD

BL	O?	OD
MO	V?	IE
FR	E?	SH
SU	N?	NY

181 The diagram shows a plan of the secret headquarters of Crime Syndicate International. By following the instructions clearly, you can reach and arrest the Boss.

N
W — E
S

Start at the square two places south of the one in the middle of the top line. Go 1 square east and 2 south. Now go 2 squares west and 4 north. The room you want is now 1 square southeast.

Which is the final square?

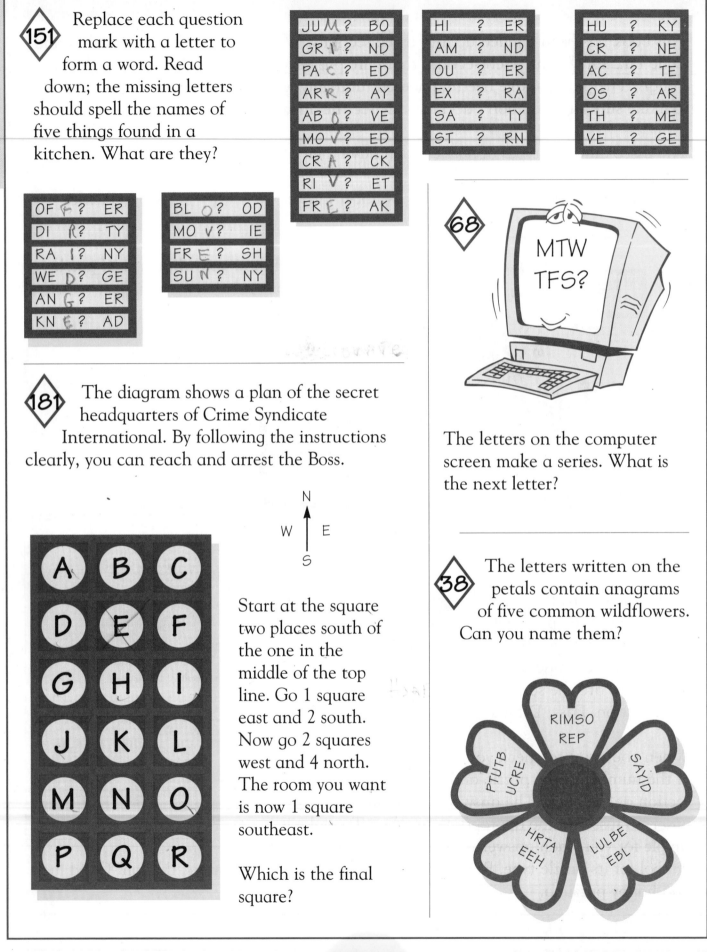

A	B	C
D	E	F
G	H	I
J	K	L
M	N	O
P	Q	R

68

MTW TFS?

The letters on the computer screen make a series. What is the next letter?

38 The letters written on the petals contain anagrams of five common wildflowers. Can you name them?

RIMSO REP

PTUTB UCRE

SAYID

HRTA EEH

LULBE EBL

103 The diagram shows a very tricky safe. Press each button in the correct order and you will be able to open the door. Which buttons do you press in which order?

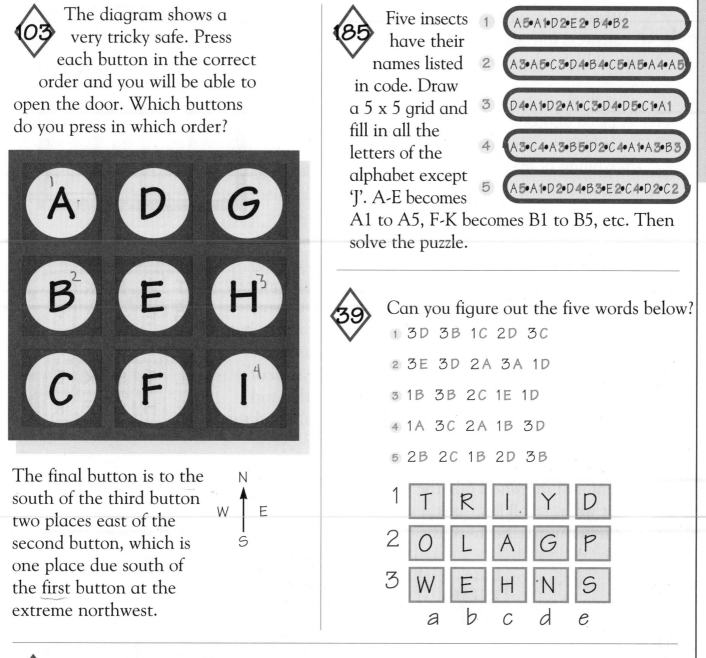

The final button is to the south of the third button two places east of the second button, which is one place due south of the first button at the extreme northwest.

N
W E
S

185 Five insects have their names listed in code. Draw a 5 x 5 grid and fill in all the letters of the alphabet except 'J'. A-E becomes A1 to A5, F-K becomes B1 to B5, etc. Then solve the puzzle.

1 A5•A1•D2•E2•B4•B2

2 A3•A5•C3•D4•B4•C5•A5•A4•A5

3 D4•A1•D2•A1•C3•D4•D5•C1•A1

4 A3•C4•A3•B5•D2•C4•A1•A3•B3

5 A5•A1•D2•D4•B3•E2•C4•D2•C2

39 Can you figure out the five words below?

1 3D 3B 1C 2D 3C

2 3E 3D 2A 3A 1D

3 1B 3B 2C 1E 1D

4 1A 3C 2A 1B 3D

5 2B 2C 1B 2D 3B

1 T R I Y D
2 O L A G P
3 W E H N S
   a b c d e

156 Replace each question mark with a letter to form a word. Reading down you should discover the names of five jobs. What are they?

PI	?	CH
ER	?	PT
FA	?	CE
AI	?	LE
CH	?	AP

AM	?	LE
FR	?	SK
HO	?	LY
WH	?	LE
WI	?	TY

VI	?	AL
GR	?	ET
DR	?	WN
UL	?	ER
ET	?	IC
GL	?	AM
HO	?	SE

ER	?	SE
MI	?	RO
FA	?	ET
CH	?	RE
RO	?	TE
FI	?	AL
WA	?	CH
GR	?	DE
LI	?	KS
WI	?	CH

JU	?	GE
WH	?	RL
PA	?	TE
NI	?	HE
MA	?	OR
BR	?	WN
DE	?	AY
JO	?	ER
EV	?	NT
RO	?	AL

109 When you solve these clues and fill the answers into the grid you will find that it reads the same down and across.

1. Not slow.
2. A piece of ground.
3. In a tennis match there are a maximum of five.
4. A piece of work to be done.

40

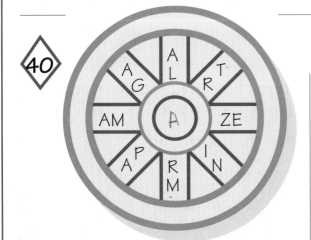

At the center of the wheel add the letter that will turn all four spokes into five-letter words. Each word starts with "A".

2 By moving one square up, down, right or left, but not diagonally, follow the trail of letters in the grid and you will find the title of a Steven Spielberg film. But beware, there are six dummy letters included.

 115 You are hunting the autograph of the movie star Mucho Macho. You know the right street but not the number. Here are some clues to help you find the house.

1. Mucho is much too macho to have flowers in his garden.
2. The number of the house cannot be divided by 7.
3. The house is not called Sunshine Cottage.
4. If the house number is divided by two the result is between 15 and 17.
5. Mucho made a film called 'Moon Mission.' It bombed.
6. Mucho is a known cat lover.

163 The new mail carrier has been given an important package to deliver to the house of the movie star Pearl Precious. The carrier doesn't know the exact number of the house but the people at the sorting office have given a few clues. See if you can help the carrier to find the right house.

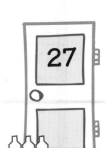

1. Pearl has no pets.
2. The number of her house cannot be divided evenly by 3.
3. Pearl does not have milk delivered.
4. Pearl hates flowers.
5. The number of the house is not a prime number.

CAR	?	RAIN
YET	?	RATE
BE	?	RATE
HER	?	LOPE
PRIME	?	ANGER
ME	?	ERE
HELL	?	PEN
MACH	?	LIVE
FIRE	?	ARK
FORGE	?	LEDGE

19 The following strings of letters are all anagrams of well-known cities. But each one contains an extra letter. The extra letters spell out one of the United States. Which one?

DILNONO   I

RAPIDS   D
Paris

AMORE   A
Rome

SHALLAD   H
Dallas

OOOKYT
Tokeo

82 To each line add a letter that will end the left word and begin the right word, to make two new words on each line. Reading down the middle column, a popular athlete will be revealed. Who?

195 The names of two famous cartoon heroes have been hidden in this frame. Who are they?

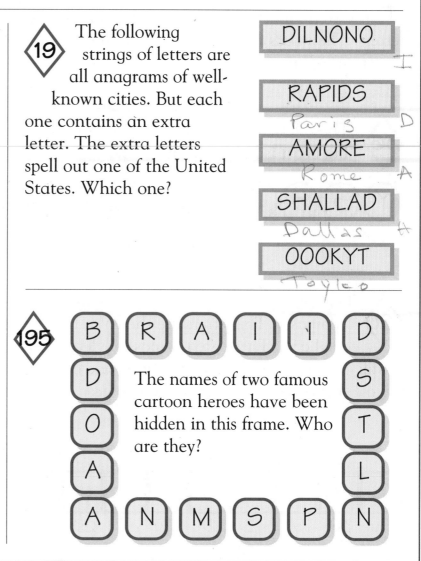

EASY

134

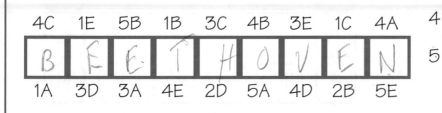

Identify 10 animals and fish concealed among the letters. The words may run in straight lines in any direction and may overlap.

67 This fairy-tale character became confused after failing to recognize her grandmother. Who is she?

Little Red Riding Hood

36 These letters are an anagram of a species of dinosaur. Can you figure out which big beast is hidden in the puzzle?

Tyrannosaurus Rex

160 The word frame below gives the name of a composer. The letters are shown in the coded grid. There are two possible letters to fill each square of the word frame, one correct, the other incorrect. Who is the composer?

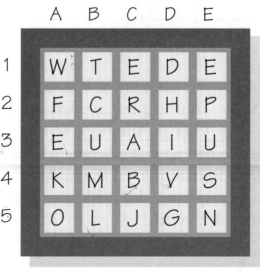

	A	B	C	D	E
1	W	T	E	D	E
2	F	C	R	H	P
3	E	U	A	I	U
4	K	M	B	V	S
5	O	L	J	G	N

4C	1E	5B	1B	3C	4B	3E	1C	4A
B	E	E	T	H	O	V	E	N
1A	3D	3A	4E	2D	5A	4D	2B	5E

6

	A	B	C	D	E
1	G	R	T	J	E
2	P	K	C	B	W
3	Y	X	F	I	H
4	U	N	Z	A	O
5	M	D	S	V	L

5A 4E 2B 1E 1C 4D 5C 1B 4B
☐ ☐ ☐ ☐ ☐ ☐ ☐ ☐ ☐
1D 3D 1E 1C 1B 3A 4C 4E 1E

The word frame above gives the name of a famous boxer. You have to decide which of the two letters from the grid on the left are correct.

121 Try to find out the name of this fairy-tale character. Come to think of it, that was the point of the story!

SLIP MILK ENTRUSTS ?

28 Which five well-known books do these newspaper headlines describe?

GIRL IN RABBIT HOLE DRAMA CLAIMS BIZARRE ADVENTURE

MISSISSIPPI BOY — PRESUMED DEAD — RETURNS WITH TREASURE

TRANSYLVANIAN COUNT WANTED ON ASSAULT CHARGES FLEES TO ENGLAND

MARINER CLAIMS STRANGE ADVENTURE AMONG TINY PEOPLE

SMALL BOY IN MOUSE TRANSFORMATION - SHOCKING WITCHCRAFT ALLEGATION

180

BU♥♥♠♦	YELLOW SPREAD
♥O♥♥♠♦	UNSTEADY WALK
BA♦♦♠♣	CONTAINS WATER
♣ONG♠♦	INCREASED LENGTH
♦UBB♣♣	BROKEN STONES
♥O♥A♣S	SUMS

The words on the left have had letters replaced by playing card symbols. Each symbol always stands for the same letter. Can you figure out what the words should be? We have given you some clues to help.

DIFFICULT

55 Look carefully at the following "words". If you replace the numbers with Roman numerals you should be able to read them easily.

1000 e 500 1 u 1000
100 0 1 50 e 500
a 100 a 500 e 1000 1 100
500 1 5 1 500 e 500
100 50 0 u 500 e 500

98 Can you find a nine-letter word scrambled in the square?

B R I
C O A
T A C

143 Look at the words on this moon map. They form an anagram of a site of lunar topography.

QI OUR FATTY ALIENS

76 All the answers to the clues opposite are five-letter words. When you have written them in the grid, you will be able to read the names of two signs of the zodiac down the first and last columns. Which ones?

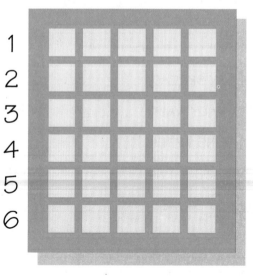

1
2
3
4
5
6

1. To move around quietly
2. Someone who says you were with them when the crime was committed.
3. You have these on fingers and toes.
4. One who makes you laugh for a living.
5. Bird of prey.
6. A train runs on these.

188 The following figures, representing certain letters, make up a ten-letter word. Solve the clues to find out which one.

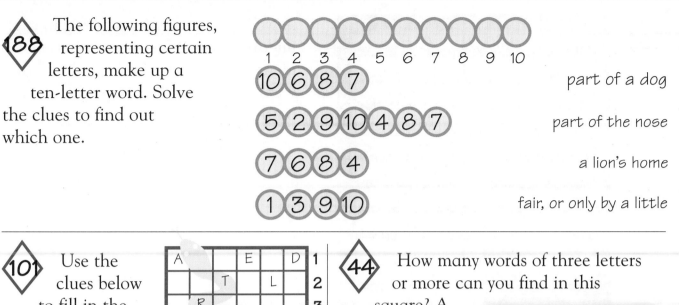

◯ ◯ ◯ ◯ ◯ ◯ ◯ ◯ ◯ ◯
1 2 3 4 5 6 7 8 9 10

10 6 8 7 — part of a dog

5 2 9 10 4 8 7 — part of the nose

7 6 8 4 — a lion's home

1 3 9 10 — fair, or only by a little

---

101 Use the clues below to fill in the words on the grid. The grid has some letters to help you start. You will find a word written along the snake.

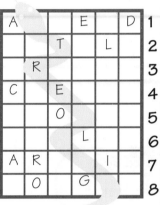

A			E		D	1
		T		L		2
	R					3
C		E				4
		O				5
			L			6
A	R			I		7
	O		G			8

1. Go up
2. Fight
3. Middle East
4. Happy
5. Metal
6. Large birds of prey
7. Frozen north
8. Branches

44 How many words of three letters or more can you find in this square? A computer found 95, but since you don't have a microchip in your head you shouldn't expect to get as many. A score of 15 is good, 25 is very good, and 40 or more is excellent. Can you find the five seven-letter words?

O	L	I
B	H	E
S	G	B

---

117 Use the clues below to fill in the missing words and complete the spiral. The last letter of each word is the first letter of the next word. The number of letters for each answer is given after the clue.

1. Pay this in class or teacher won't be pleased (9)
2. This is most of the air we breathe (8)
3. Lump of gold (6)
4. You can bear it – just about! (9)
5. Weird (5)
6. Aubergine (8)
7. The hare won't always beat him in the race (8)
8. The person who saw the crime (10)
9. A noisy quarrel (8)
10. Pronouncing words properly (9)
11. Zero (7)

162

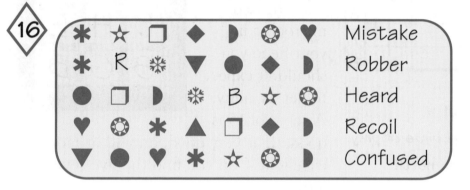

	?	
HALLO	?	ASH
SCAMP	?	DEAL
AWAKE	?	EON
CAME	?	WE
ARISE	?	AILS
ARE	?	KIN
PEA	?	EACH
BUS	?	OWL
JOSTLE	?	ARK
HOP	?	VENT
STRANGE	?	ANKLE

A well-known actress is hiding in the middle column. To discover her identity, find a letter that will end the word on the left and begin the word on the right, creating two brand new words on each line. Who is she?

16

Mistake

Robber

Heard

Recoil

Confused

The seven letter words to the left are all in code. The same symbol always stands for the same letter. To help you, a clue is given at the end of each line and two letters have been left uncoded.

88

Use all the letters in the grid twice to give you two nine-letter words.
The clue is: "silent lady killers".

N	O	L
I	S	S
E	S	E

196

Transform the top word into the bottom one by altering one letter each time and making a new word with each move.

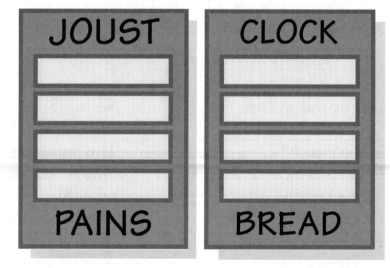

JOUST

PAINS

CLOCK

BREAD

133 The words in the box have something in common. Which of the following words fits with them?

cup
group
proud
buds
jogs

?

kill

then

bugs

70 Match the following words with their position on the body shown.

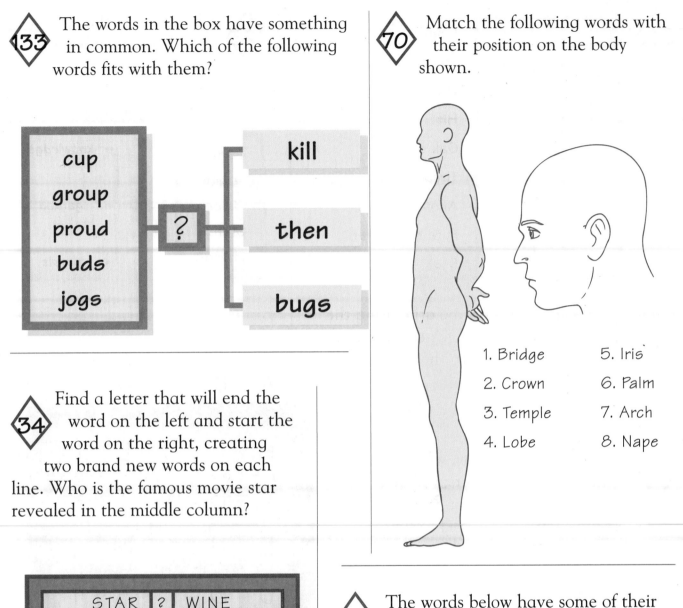

1. Bridge
2. Crown
3. Temple
4. Lobe
5. Iris
6. Palm
7. Arch
8. Nape

34 Find a letter that will end the word on the left and start the word on the right, creating two brand new words on each line. Who is the famous movie star revealed in the middle column?

STAR	?	WINE
HELL	?	MISSION
FAR	?	ASK
AMNESIA	?	REST
ANGLE	?	AFTER
MEN	?	NIT
CHILL	?	SLAM
TUB	?	HOE
SHIN	?	BONY

152 The words below have some of their letters replaced by symbols. Each symbol always represents the same letter. To help you we have also put in some clues.

✿	■	◗	>	+	◗	Trading without money
✿	■	♥	♥	✓	✓ N	Party floater
C	◗	+	■	>	+	Make
>	◗	■	D +	◗		Dealer
♥	✓	✓	>	+	◗	Plunderer
✿	+	◗	■	>	+	Scold harshly

DIFFICULT

1

		G		
			N	
		C		
				K
		O		
A				
	L			
			S	
	E			

Finger

Menial workers

Desert plants

Hit

Oak seed

Tired pains

Another name

Pure happiness

Step

Fill in the missing words on the grid, using the letters we have given and the clues on the side. Find the word that runs down the snake.

123 The words in the left-hand box have been chosen according to a simple system. Can any of the words outside join them?

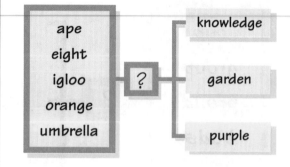

26 The word frame below, when filled with the correct letters, will give the name of a Caribbean island. The letters are shown in the grid to the right. There are two possible letters to fill each square, one correct, the other incorrect. What is the island?

2B	1B	2E	3A	3C	5C	2D	1A
3E	4A	3D	1D	1B	4E	1C	4B

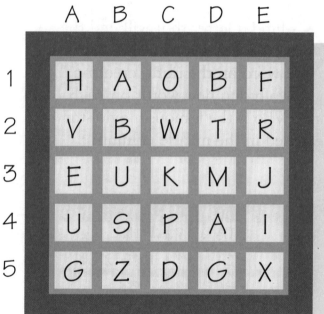

176

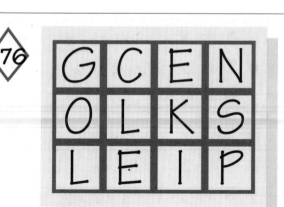

Move from square to touching square, including diagonals, and using all the letters, find a musical instrument.

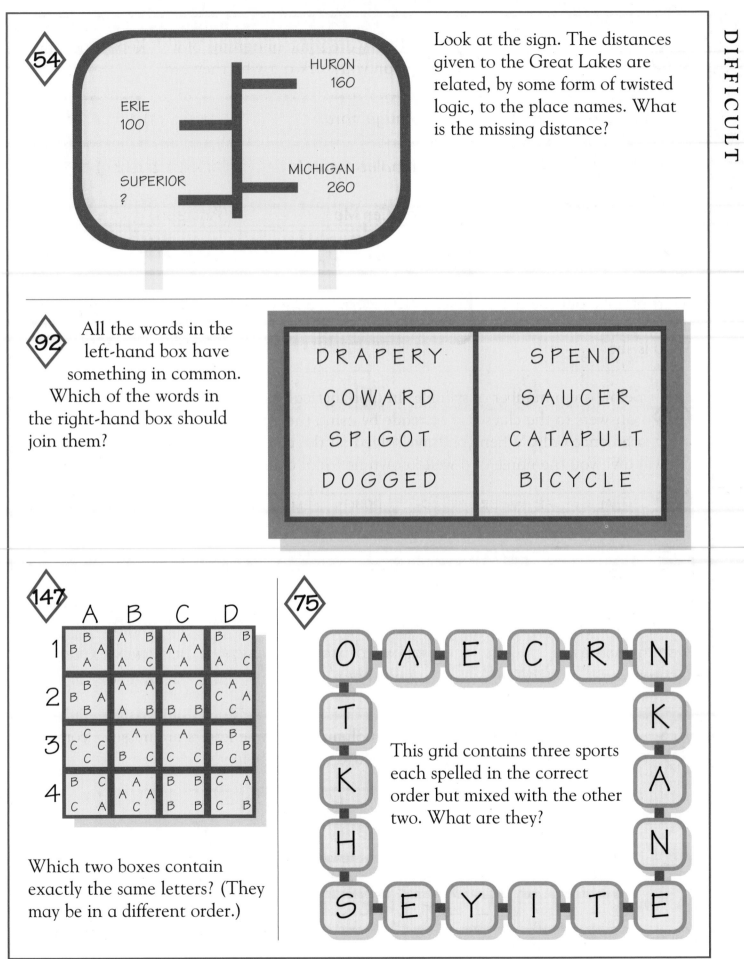

54

HURON 160

ERIE 100

SUPERIOR ?

MICHIGAN 260

Look at the sign. The distances given to the Great Lakes are related, by some form of twisted logic, to the place names. What is the missing distance?

92 All the words in the left-hand box have something in common. Which of the words in the right-hand box should join them?

DRAPERY
COWARD
SPIGOT
DOGGED

SPEND
SAUCER
CATAPULT
BICYCLE

147

	A	B	C	D
1	B B A	A A C	A A A	B B A C
2	B A B	A A B	C C B B	A C C
3	C C C	A B C	A C C	B B B C
4	B C C A	A A C	B B B	C A C B

Which two boxes contain exactly the same letters? (They may be in a different order.)

75

O A E C R N

T K

K A

H A

S E Y I T E N

This grid contains three sports each spelled in the correct order but mixed with the other two. What are they?

DIFFICULT

189

O H O G S
R M
O E
E T
M E R O O

?

This fairy-tale mum had a heart of gold, but she got down sometimes.
Who is she?

107 Below are some anagrams of well-known people. Can you work out who they are?

1. **G's huge bore** (Politician)

2. **C Kindles Search** (Classic author)

3. **Moodier Me** (Actress)

4. **Shy without neon** (Singer)

5. **A new antic – So?** (English scientist)

48 Below are a number of syllables in alphabetical order and a list of clues. All the answers to the clues can be made by using the syllables given. Each syllable is used **once** only. When you have solved all the clues, the first letters of the answers will give you the name of a well-known fictional character.

A	AL	AP	BRA	DI	DOUG	EM	GE	GO	IN	IT
JE	LA	LAS	LE	LEM	LY	MARE	MI	NA	NEP	NIGHT
ON	OR	OS	PER	PLE	PO	RU	SA	SA	TRICH	TUNE

1. EUROPEAN COUNTRY (5 letters)
2. FRENCH EMPEROR (8)
3. BOY'S NAME (6)
4. COLOR OF THE RAINBOW (6)

5. FRUIT (5)
6. DREAM (9)
7. BRANCH OF MATHEMATICS (7)
8. HOLY CITY (9)

9. FLIGHTLESS BIRD (7)
10. PLANET (7)
11. SUPREME RULER (7)
12. SAUSAGE (6)

114 Can you fill in the blanks? In each column, the same letters are missing from each box. The last column has an extra letter to help you.

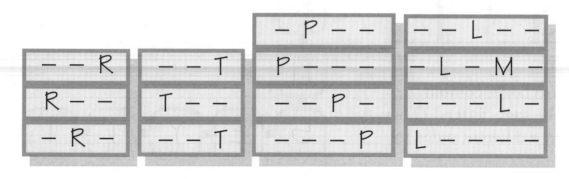

166 Here are some book titles in which all the consonants have been removed. Can you figure out the titles just from the vowels? The clues will help you.

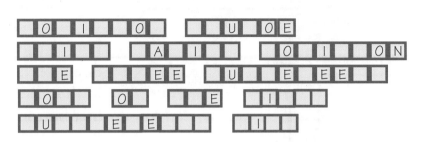

1. Desert Island. `O   I   O      U   O E`
2. Another island, same name! `I      A I      O   I   O N`
3. All for one! `E      E E   U   E   E E`
4. Middle Earth `O      O      E      I`
5. Adventurous lad `U      E   E      I`

---

17 The unpronounceable jumbles below are really United States without their vowels. How many of them can you unravel?

CLFRN

DH

NBRSK

HW

LSK

---

83 The following words have been coded using Greek-style letters. Each Greek symbol always stands for the same letter. If it's still Greek to you, the clues should help!

ΛΞΦΓΛΜΕΤ	HANDBONES
ΔΦΓΛΜΙΞΗ	BABY DUCK
ΙΞΛΜΙΞΗΤ	VAGUE IDEAS
ΠΙΓΛΜΙΞΗ	PRESERVING FOOD
ΙΞΓΜΦΔΕΤ	CONTAINS

---

197 In this grid there are 10 States, written in continuous straight lines. The names are written forwards or backwards, up or down, across or diagonally. Can you find them all?

The states are:

ALASKA   NEVADA
ARIZONA   NEW MEXICO
CALIFORNIA   OREGON
COLORADO   TEXAS
MONTANA   WYOMING

N	B	W	R	Y	A	V	M	D	A
X	E	J	V	D	H	A	O	I	C
H	B	W	A	C	R	K	N	A	F
Y	D	V	M	I	T	R	T	K	G
K	E	F	Z	E	O	W	A	S	N
N	Q	O	X	F	X	Q	N	A	I
B	N	A	I	G	P	I	A	L	M
A	S	L	H	C	B	F	C	A	O
P	A	J	N	O	G	E	R	O	Y
C	O	L	O	R	A	D	O	G	W

139

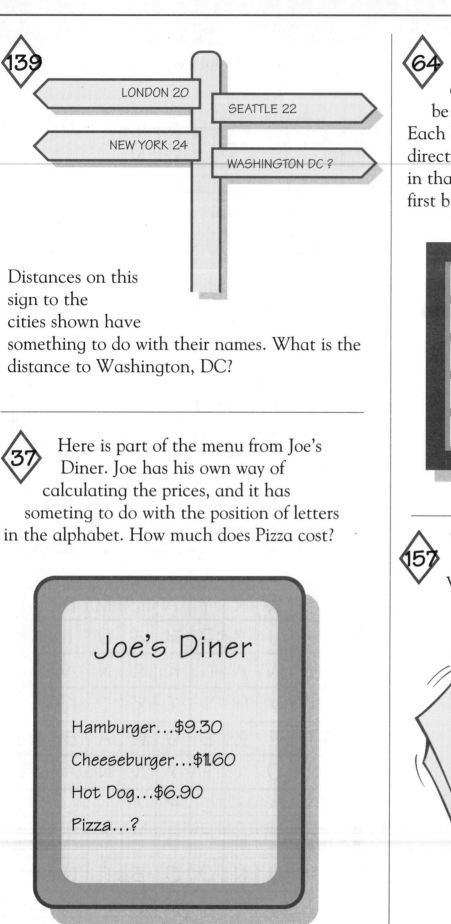

LONDON 20

SEATTLE 22

NEW YORK 24

WASHINGTON DC ?

Distances on this sign to the cities shown have something to do with their names. What is the distance to Washington, DC?

37 Here is part of the menu from Joe's Diner. Joe has his own way of calculating the prices, and it has someting to do with the position of letters in the alphabet. How much does Pizza cost?

Joe's Diner

Hamburger...$9.30

Cheeseburger...$11.60

Hot Dog...$6.90

Pizza...?

64 Here is an unusual safe. To reach the "open" button, all the other buttons must be pressed in the correct order. Each button has a compass direction and the distance to go in that direction. Which is the first button you must press?

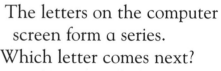

4SE	1E	4S	1SE	4SW
2S	1E	1NE	1SE	1SW
1E	1NW	OPEN	2NW	2W
3E	3NE	1SW	3NW	1SW
2N	1N	1N	3N	1N

157 The letters on the computer screen form a series. Which letter comes next?

OTTFF SSEN?

41 Figure out which letter of the alphabet is represented by each of the numbers 1 to 26 in the grid to the right. When you figure out what the numbers represent, write them in the reference grid at the bottom. To help you start, a few letters have been given. The completed puzzle will look like a filled-in crossword, containing only genuine words.

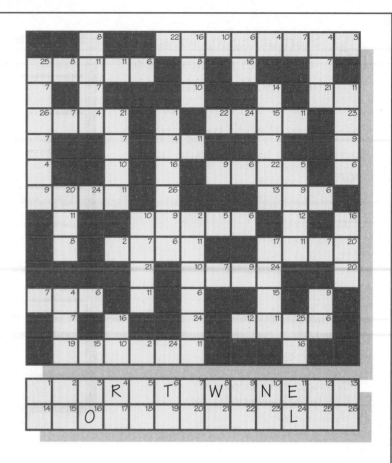

122 Look at the diagrams, crack the logic of the puzzle, and discover the missing letters.

27 Look at the letters below. They all share one strange property. What is it?

EHIKOX

178 Look at the sign below. The distances given are related, by some form of twisted logic, to the place names. Can you figure out the logic and then replace the question mark with the correct distance?

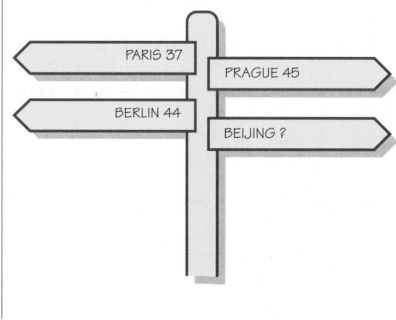

21

VERY TOUGH

56 Start at the top left square and fill in the answers to the clues. Follow the grid in a spiral to the center. The last two letters of each word are also the first two letters of the next word.

1. Wild dog (6)
2. Water tortoise (8)
3. Discoverer of new ideas (8)
4. Musical instrument (5)
5. Story (8)
6. Used for long distance conversation (9)
7. Worn for decoration (8)
8. Eaten at breakfast (6)
9. Type of math (7)
10. Demanded by kidnappers (6)
11. Sign to the superstitious (4)
12. Holds a letter (8)
13. Fruit (4)
14. Reach your destination (6)
15. Pest (6)
16. Crazy (6)
17. Closer (6)
18. Mistake (5)
19. Music makers (10)
20. To do with fortune telling using the stars (12)

95 The letters below can be fitted into the grid so that they answer the clues across the grid and make a word down the middle.

PBTTFAYCUSDEANRA

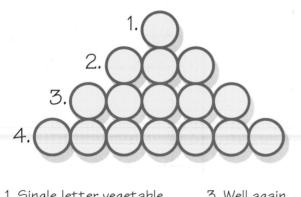

1. Single letter vegetable
2. Nocturnal flying animal
3. Well again
4. Imagination

137 The letters on the computer screen make a series. Figure out the logic and find out what comes next.

AEAPAU UUECO?

77 Now, this may look like a number puzzle, but it isn't. It is definitely a word puzzle. Why are some numbers above the line?

$$\frac{1\ 2 \qquad 6 \qquad 10}{3\ 4\ 5 \quad 7\ 8\ 9}$$

184 Start at the top left corner and fill in the answers to the clues, working around the grid in a spiral. The last two letters of each answer form the first two of the next. The number of letters in each answer is given in parentheses after the clue.

1. Capital of UK (6)
2. Vegetable (5)
3. One time only (4)
4. Stop completely (5)
5. Quite a few (7)
6. Permit (5)
7. Possessor (5)
8. Rub out (5)
9. Older (6)
10. Command (5)
11. Historical periods (4)
12. Study of the stars (9)
13. Gold, Frankincense and – – – – – (5)
14. Words with similar endings (eg. Prime time) (5)
15. Given by the doctor (8)
16. Uneasy (7)
17. Everyday (5)
18. Boy with magic lamp (7)
19. Not seen (9)
20. Citrus fruit (5)
21. Single unit (3)
22. More recent (5)
23. Wipe out completely (9)
24. Extreme fear (6)
25. Groups of fruit trees (8)

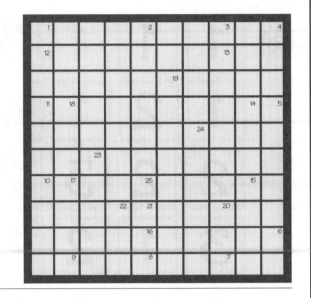

108 Just a brief message, in order but with the vowels and spaces removed. Can you figure it out?

FYTHNKTHSSGNGTB
SYYHDBTTRTHNKGN

50 The following clues will give you the names of six sports. Read the first letters of the words in order and you will discover bigger game.

TAKE A DIVE	
HIT THE EYE	
US OR UK?	
THE GENERAL	
THEY'RE OFF	
GOOD WITH FIGURES	

118 Can you crack this fiendish crossword? It won't be easy.

ACROSS
1. What supports the ship? It's in front of the Head (4)
6. Doubly bereaved (6)
8. He may be short, but he's your father's mother's husband's son (2)
9. Take it back and nurture it (4)
10. Measure your influence at the royal court (5)
12. In the heat, they're just my cup of tea (6)
13. The active principle (2)
14. Good news for moles – no need to take up rock climbing (4)
16. This is one male stuck in a rut. Oh dear. Get the point? (4)
18. Everything slipped into place, it seems. It should stay there, too (3)
19. A wild stallion? From tiny acorns... (4)
21. Open to the secrets beyond? A guardian waits between... (4)
23. Leads the way, confined (8)

DOWN
1. Broken? It's not the first. What a way to start a day (7)
2. The key to multiple being (3)
3. Illumination? How clever (5)
4. Winged one, what's the rush? (6)
5. Just one long arm, but this time it's outside the Law (6)
7. Sharp, to a camel's eye (6)
11. Tumbling free? How divine (6)
15. Ice castles – a chilly idea (5)
16. Fooled you! It's just juice (3)
17. Me too? It's all so additive (4)
19. Run the long way (3)
20. 2+2 is 4. That's sumthing (3)
22. Logically, there's no way you can have both (2)

EASY

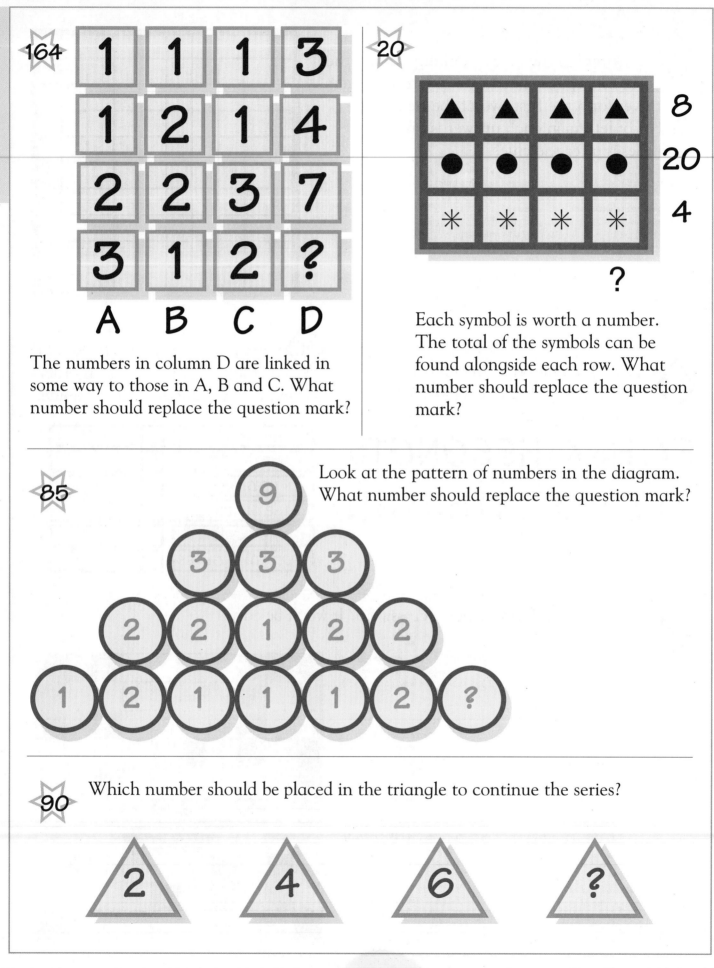

164

1 1 1 3
1 2 1 4
2 2 3 7
3 1 2 ?

A B C D

The numbers in column D are linked in some way to those in A, B and C. What number should replace the question mark?

20

8
20
4
?

Each symbol is worth a number. The total of the symbols can be found alongside each row. What number should replace the question mark?

85

9
3 3 3
2 2 1 2 2
1 2 1 1 1 2 ?

Look at the pattern of numbers in the diagram. What number should replace the question mark?

90

Which number should be placed in the triangle to continue the series?

2   4   6   ?

148

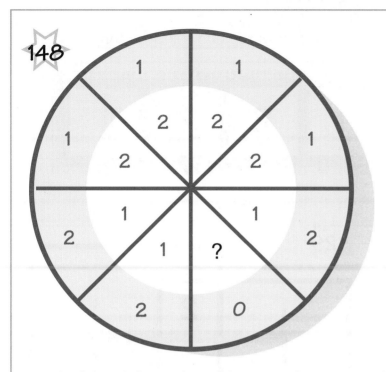

Each slice of this cake adds up to the same value. What number should replace the question mark?

63 How many squares of any size can you find in this diagram ?

35

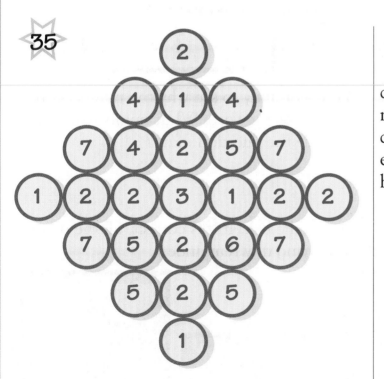

Start at the middle and move from circle to touching circle. Collect three numbers and add them to your starting 3. How many different routes are there to a total of 8?

153 Move from the bottom left-hand circle to the top right-hand one, following the arrows, adding together all five numbers. Each dark circle is worth 1 and this should be added to your total each time you meet one. What is the highest total you can reach?

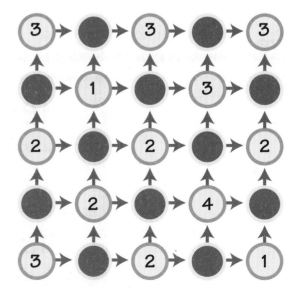

EASY

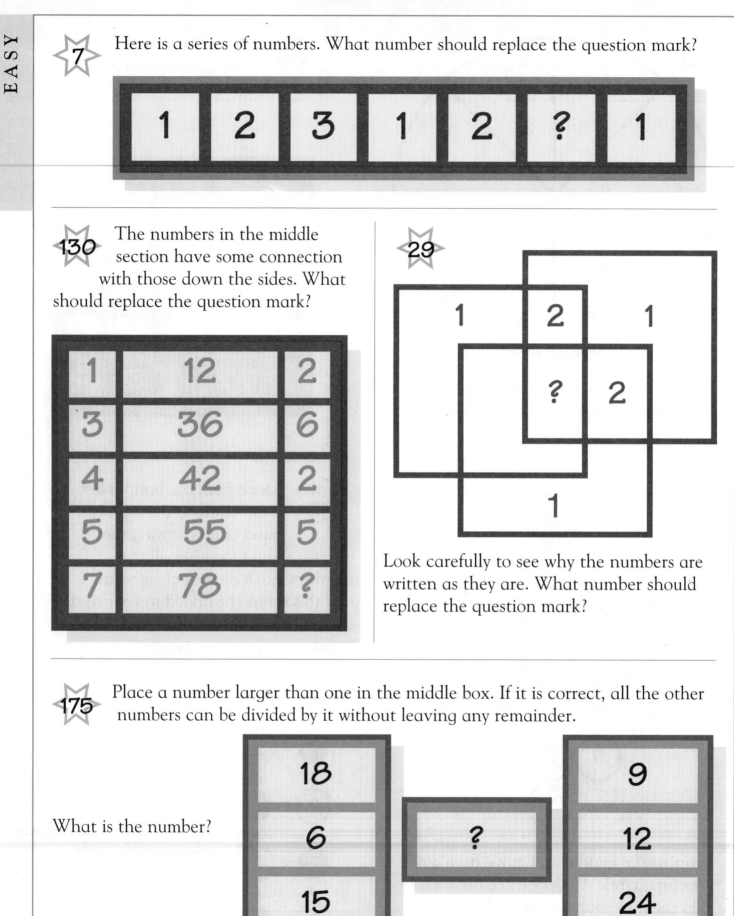

7 Here is a series of numbers. What number should replace the question mark?

| 1 | 2 | 3 | 1 | 2 | ? | 1 |

130 The numbers in the middle section have some connection with those down the sides. What should replace the question mark?

1	12	2
3	36	6
4	42	2
5	55	5
7	78	?

29

1   2   1

?   2

1

Look carefully to see why the numbers are written as they are. What number should replace the question mark?

175 Place a number larger than one in the middle box. If it is correct, all the other numbers can be divided by it without leaving any remainder.

What is the number?

| 18 |
| 6 |
| 15 |

?

| 9 |
| 12 |
| 24 |

EASY

57 What is the lowest number of lines needed to divide the elephant so that you can find the numbers 1, 2, 3 and 4 in each section?

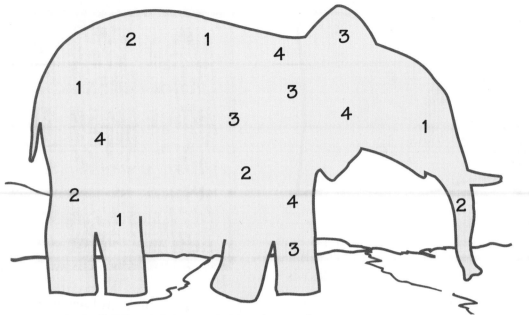

96 Replace each question mark with either a plus, minus, multiply or divide sign. Each sign can be used more than once. When the correct ones have been used the sum will be completed. What are the signs?

150 Start at any outer corner and follow the lines. Add up the first four numbers you come to and then add on your starting corner number. What is the lowest you can score?

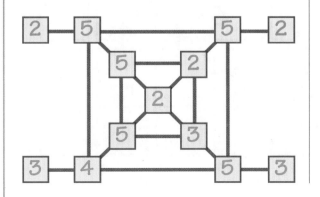

74 Each slice of this cake adds up to the same number. In each ring, the numbers total 32. Which numbers should appear in the blank spaces?

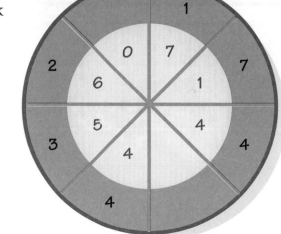

EASY

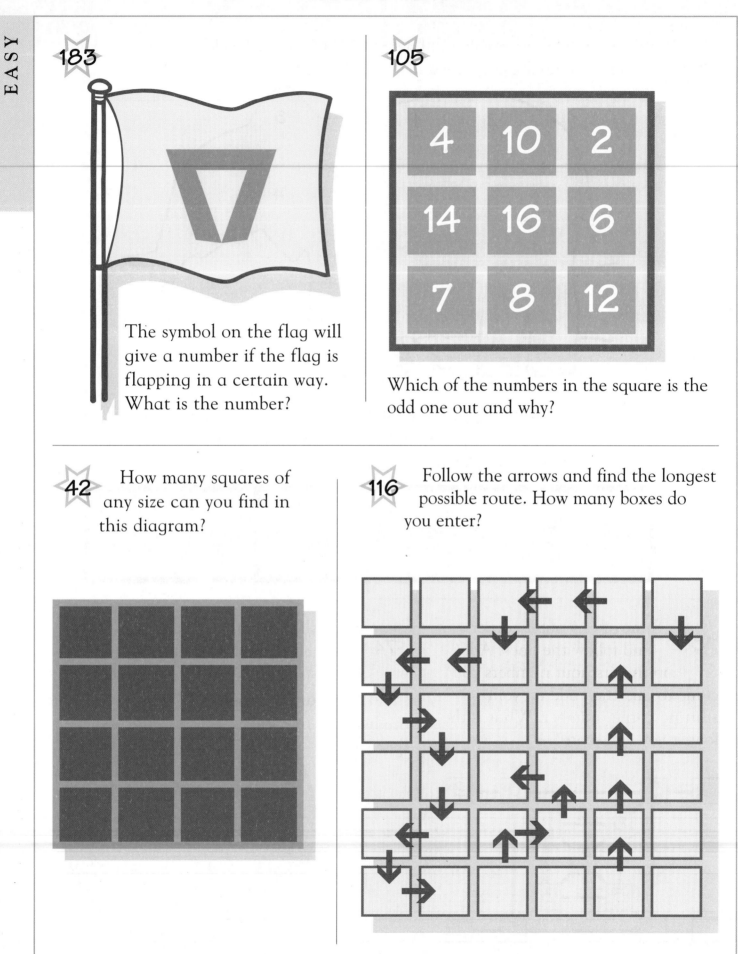

183

The symbol on the flag will give a number if the flag is flapping in a certain way. What is the number?

105

4	10	2
14	16	6
7	8	12

Which of the numbers in the square is the odd one out and why?

42 How many squares of any size can you find in this diagram?

116 Follow the arrows and find the longest possible route. How many boxes do you enter?

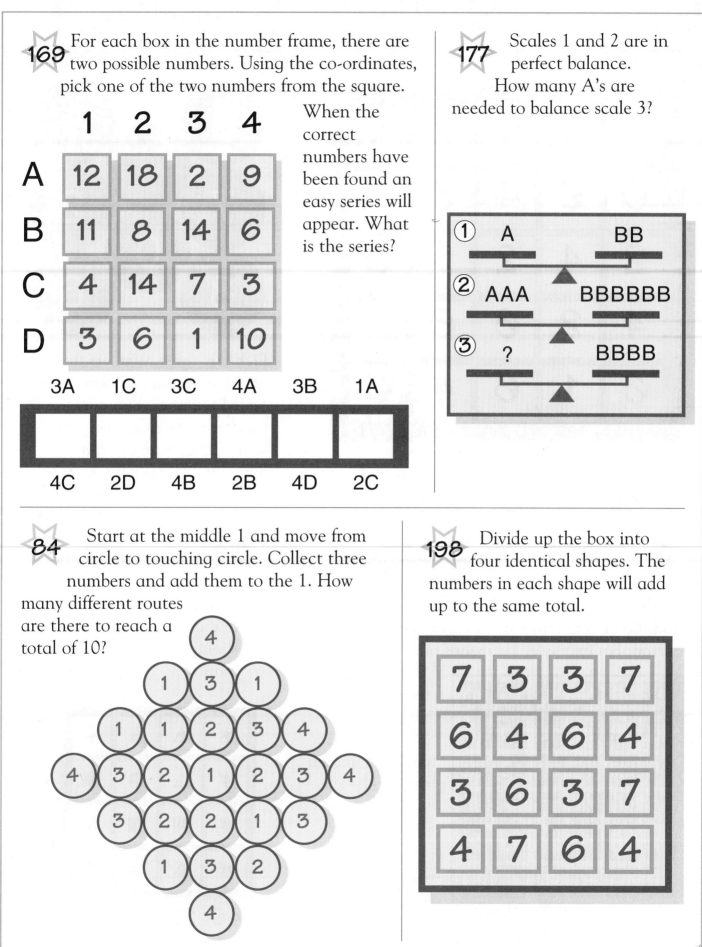

169 For each box in the number frame, there are two possible numbers. Using the co-ordinates, pick one of the two numbers from the square.

When the correct numbers have been found an easy series will appear. What is the series?

	1	2	3	4
A	12	18	2	9
B	11	8	14	6
C	4	14	7	3
D	3	6	1	10

3A	1C	3C	4A	3B	1A
4C	2D	4B	2B	4D	2C

177 Scales 1 and 2 are in perfect balance. How many A's are needed to balance scale 3?

① A   BB

② AAA   BBBBBB

③ ?   BBBB

84 Start at the middle 1 and move from circle to touching circle. Collect three numbers and add them to the 1. How many different routes are there to reach a total of 10?

198 Divide up the box into four identical shapes. The numbers in each shape will add up to the same total.

7	3	3	7
6	4	6	4
3	6	3	7
4	7	6	4

29

DIFFICULT

135

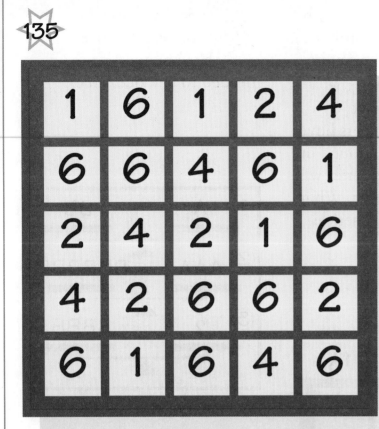

Divide the box using four lines so that each part adds up to the same total. How is this done?

66

Pick any three numbers from above that make a total of ten added together. You may use a number more than once. The same three numbers in a different order don't count. How many ways are there?

32 Here is an unusual safe. Each of the buttons must be pressed exactly once in the correct order to open it. The last button is marked F. The number of moves and the direction to move in is marked on each button. For example, 1U means one move up.

Which button is the first you must press? Here's a clue: it can be found on the middle row.

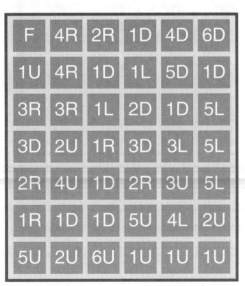

F	4R	2R	1D	4D	6D
1U	4R	1D	1L	5D	1D
3R	3R	1L	2D	1D	5L
3D	2U	1R	3D	3L	5L
2R	4U	1D	2R	3U	5L
1R	1D	1D	5U	4L	2U
5U	2U	6U	1U	1U	1U

159 Each symbol has a value. The total of the symbols can be found alongside each row and column. What number should replace the question mark?

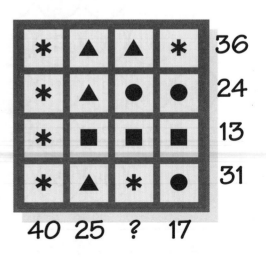

✱	▲	▲	✱	36
✱	▲	●	●	24
✱	■	■	■	13
✱	▲	✱	●	31
40	25	?	17	

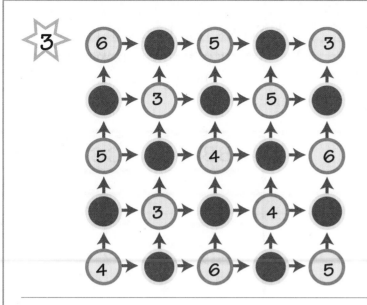

★ 3

Move from the bottom left-hand circle to the top right-hand one adding together all five numbers. Each dark circle is worth minus 1, and so 1 should be taken away from your total each time you meet one. What is the highest total you can find?

★ 125 Each of the buttons on this safe must be pressed exactly once in the correct order to open it. The last button is marked F. The number of moves and the direction to move in is marked on each button. For example, 1U means one move up. Which button is the first you must press? Here's a clue: it can be found on the middle row.

F	4R	1D	6D	2L	6D
5D	1U	1R	2R	4L	2D
4R	1L	3R	2U	4D	2L
2R	1L	1D	2D	3L	2D
1R	3U	2U	2R	1U	1L
1U	3U	2R	1U	5U	5L
6U	1U	1U	1L	5U	4L

★ 25 If you look carefully you should see the pattern. What number should replace the question mark?

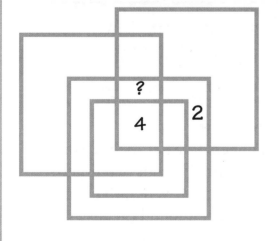

★ 179 Start at the middle and move from circle to touching circle. Collect three numbers and add them to the 2. How many different routes are there to make a total of 12?

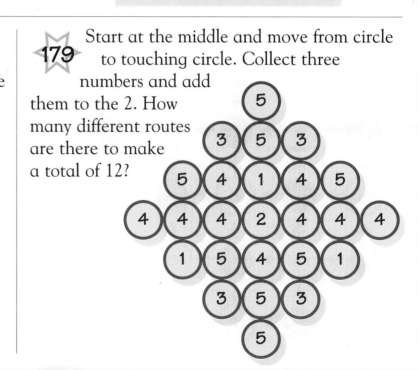

DIFFICULT

51 Which of these images is not of the same box?

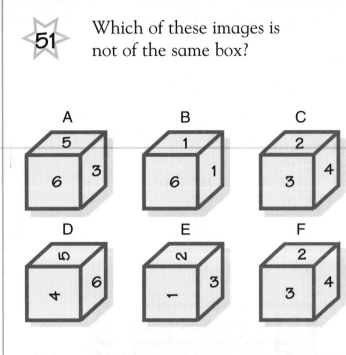

93 Scales 1 and 2 are in perfect balance. If one C is worth four As, how many As are needed to balance scale 3?

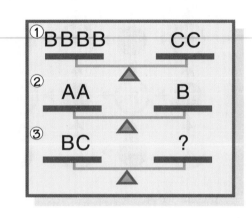

141 Move from the bottom left-hand circle to the top right-hand one by following the arrows and adding together all five numbers. Each dark circle is worth minus 3 and so 3 should be taken from your total each time you meet one. What is the highest total you can find?

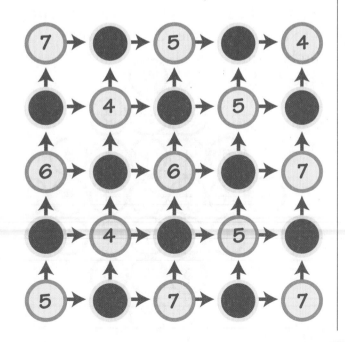

71

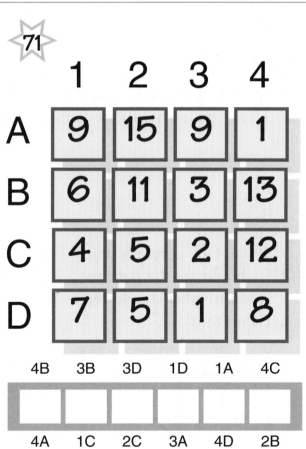

For each box in the frame, there are two possible numbers to be chosen. Using the co-ordinates, chose one of two numbers from the square grid. When the correct numbers have been found an easy series will appear. What is the series?

182 Press each of the buttons of this secure safe exactly once, and in the correct order, to open it. The last button is marked F. The number of moves and the direction to move in is marked on each button. For example 1U means one move up. Which button is the first you must press? Here's a clue: it can be found on the top row.

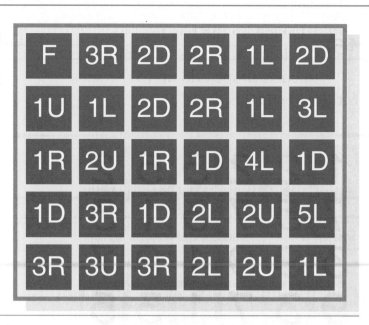

F	3R	2D	2R	1L	2D
1U	1L	2D	2R	1L	3L
1R	2U	1R	1D	4L	1D
1D	3R	1D	2L	2U	5L
3R	3U	3R	2L	2U	1L

106

If the flag is folded a certain way, the symbol will give a number. What is it?

49

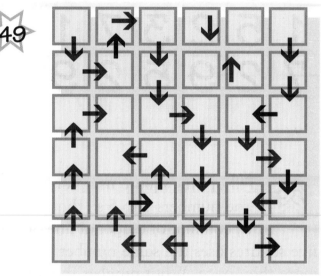

Follow the arrows and find the longest possible route. How many boxes have been entered?

120

1	2	3	4	5
3			1	2
		?		

Fill up this square using only the numbers one to five so that no row, column, or diagonal line of five squares uses the same number more than once. What number should replace the question mark?

161 Divide up the box into six identical shapes. The numbers in each shape add up to the same total. How is this done?

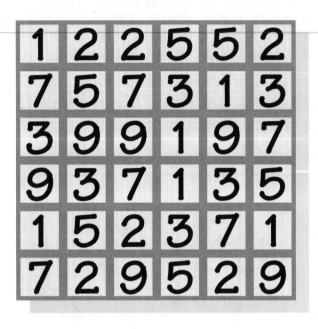

1	2	2	5	5	2
7	5	7	3	1	3
3	9	9	1	9	7
9	3	7	1	3	5
1	5	2	3	7	1
7	2	9	5	2	9

89 Fill up this square using only the numbers 1 to 5 so that no row, column, or diagonal line of five squares uses the same number more than once. What number should replace the question mark?

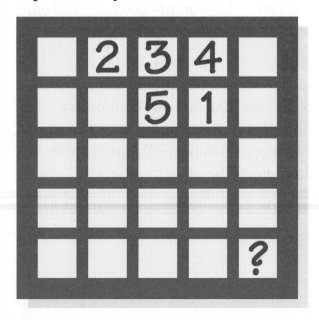

13

	1	2	3	4
A	7	16	11	4
B	1	12	18	3
C	9	13	8	14
D	5	2	17	2

4D	2C	4A	1A	3A	3D
1B	4B	1D	3C	1C	2C

For each box in the frame, there are two possible numbers. Using the co-ordinates, choose one of two numbers from the square grid. When the correct numbers have been found an easy series will appear. What is the series?

191 Scales 1 and 2 are in perfect balance. How many Cs are needed to balance scale 3?

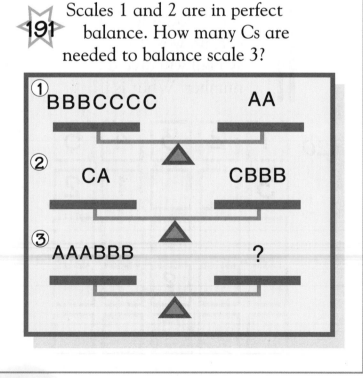

34

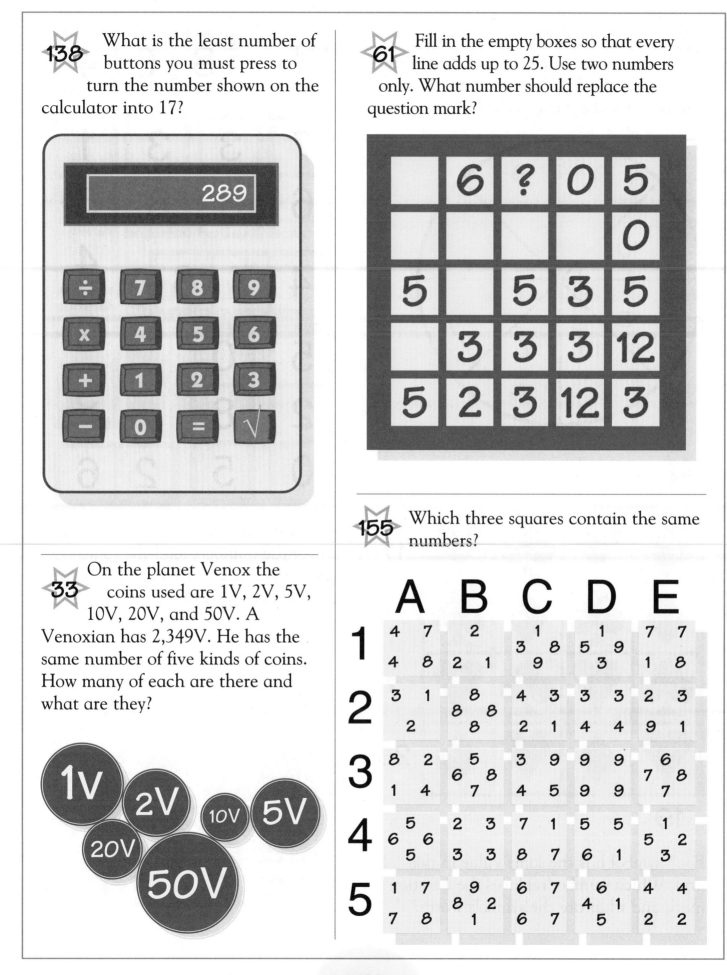

138 What is the least number of buttons you must press to turn the number shown on the calculator into 17?

289

61 Fill in the empty boxes so that every line adds up to 25. Use two numbers only. What number should replace the question mark?

	6	?	0	5
				0
5		5	3	5
	3	3	3	12
5	2	3	12	3

155 Which three squares contain the same numbers?

33 On the planet Venox the coins used are 1V, 2V, 5V, 10V, 20V, and 50V. A Venoxian has 2,349V. He has the same number of five kinds of coins. How many of each are there and what are they?

1V 2V 10V 5V 20V 50V

	A	B	C	D	E
1	4 7 / 4 8	2 / 2 1	1 3 8 / 9	1 5 9 / 3	7 7 / 1 8
2	3 1 / 2	8 8 8 / 8	4 3 / 2 1	3 3 / 4 4	2 3 / 9 1
3	8 2 / 1 4	5 6 8 / 7	3 9 / 4 5	9 9 / 9 9	6 / 7 8 / 7
4	5 / 6 6 / 5	2 3 / 3 3	7 1 / 8 7	5 5 / 6 1	1 / 5 2 / 3
5	1 7 / 7 8	9 / 8 2 / 1	6 7 / 6 7	6 / 4 1 / 5	4 4 / 2 2

35

DIFFICULT

 10 Each slice of this cake adds up to the same number. Each ring of the cake also has the same total. Which number should appear in the blanks?

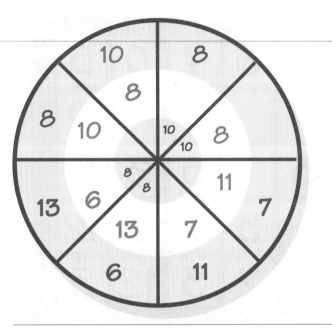

24

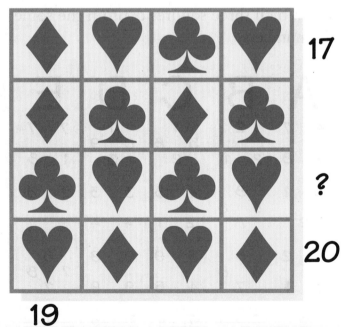

17

?

20

19

Each symbol has the same value in this grid. Which number replaces the question mark and what are the symbols worth?

129

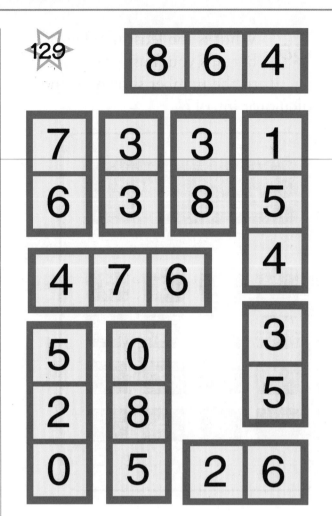

Arrange these pieces to form a square where the numbers read the same horizontally and vertically. What does the finished square look like?

172 Which numbers replace the question marks?

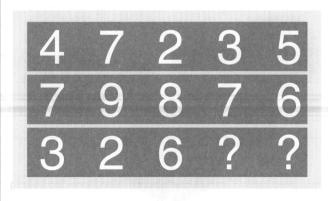

DIFFICULT

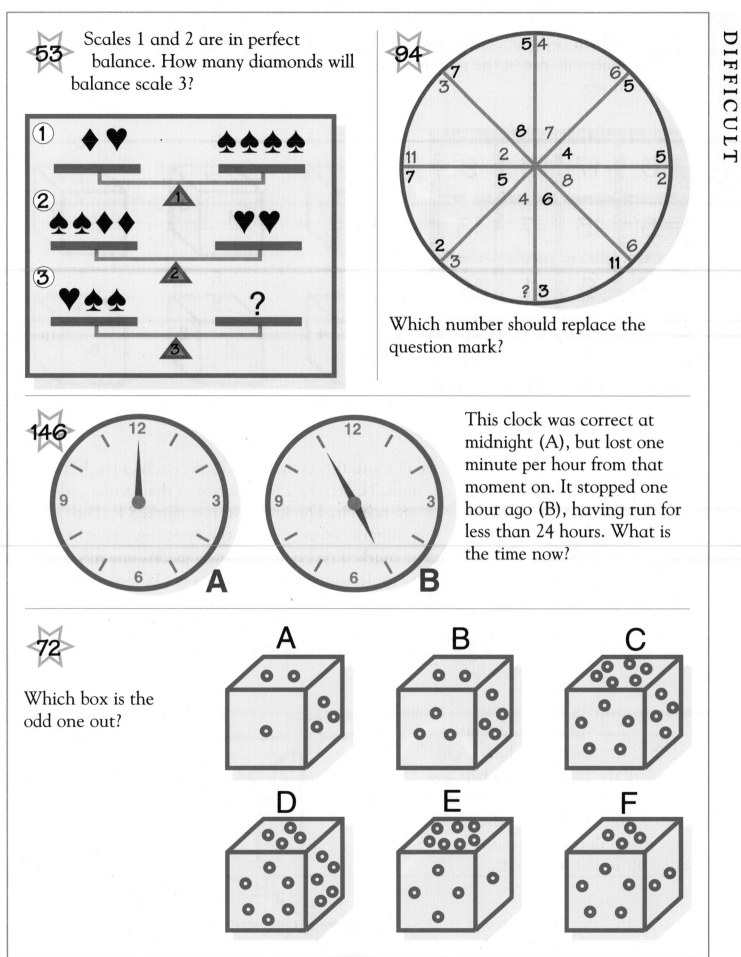

53 Scales 1 and 2 are in perfect balance. How many diamonds will balance scale 3?

94 Which number should replace the question mark?

146 This clock was correct at midnight (A), but lost one minute per hour from that moment on. It stopped one hour ago (B), having run for less than 24 hours. What is the time now?

A

B

72 Which box is the odd one out?

A   B   C

D   E   F

187 Which two numbers on the square do not fit the pattern and why?

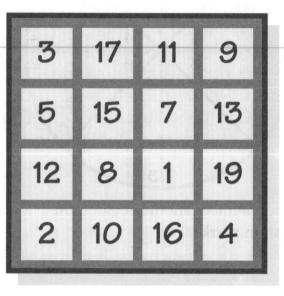

104 Which of these pictures is not of the same box?

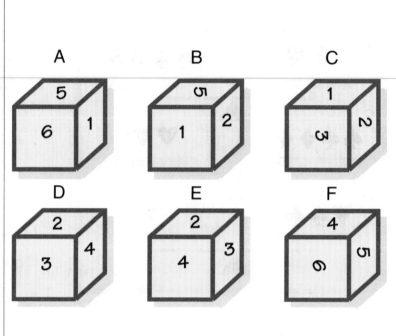

43

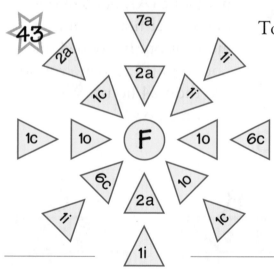

To get into this complicated safe, each of the buttons must be pressed exactly once in the correct order to open it. The last button is marked F. The number of moves and the direction to move in is marked on each button. 1i means one move in, while 1o means one move out. 1c means one move clockwise and 1a means one move counter clockwise. Which button is the first you must press? Here's a clue: it is in the inner circle.

112 Start at any outer corner and follow the lines. Add up the first four numbers you meet and then add your starting corner number. What is the lowest possible total and how many different routes lead to it?

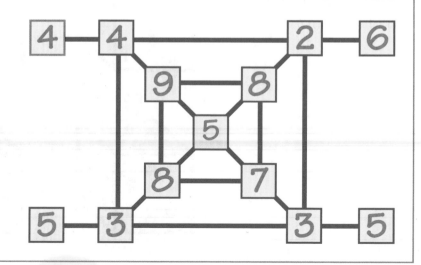

168 Which three squares contain the same numbers?

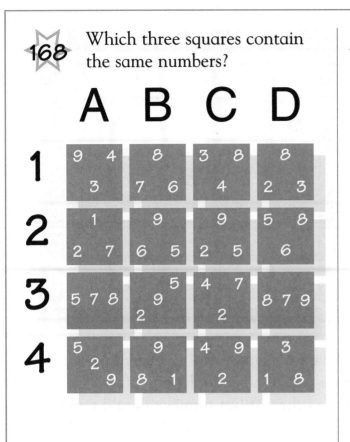

58 Move via touching circles from the bottom left-hand "5" to the top right-hand "3". Add all nine numbers together. What is the highest you can score?

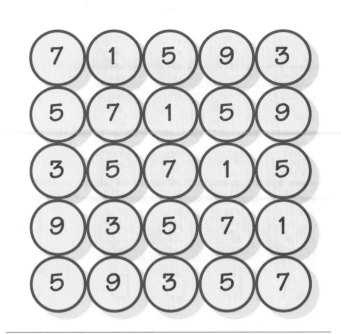

87 If you look carefully you should see why the numbers are written as they are. What number should replace the question mark?

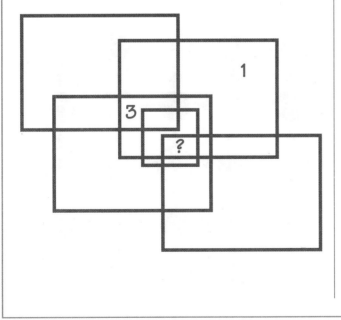

199 Fill up this square with the numbers one to five so that no row, column, or diagonal line of five squares uses the same number more than once. What number should replace the question mark?

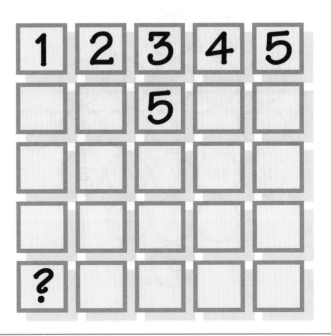

VERY TOUGH

136 The numbers in column D are linked in some way to those in A, B and C. What number should replace the question mark?

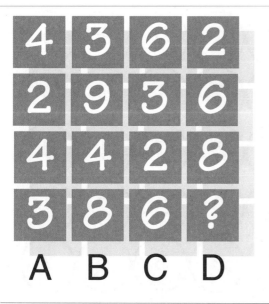

A   B   C   D

62

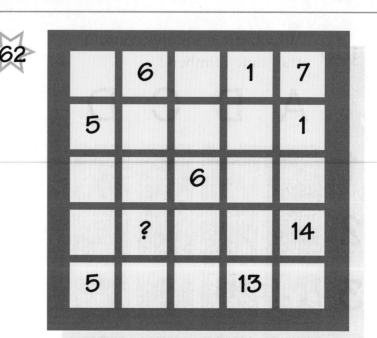

Fill in the empty boxes so that every line adds up to 30. Use two numbers only, one of which is double the other. What number should replace the question mark?

31 Look at the pattern of the numbers in the diagram. What number should replace the question mark?

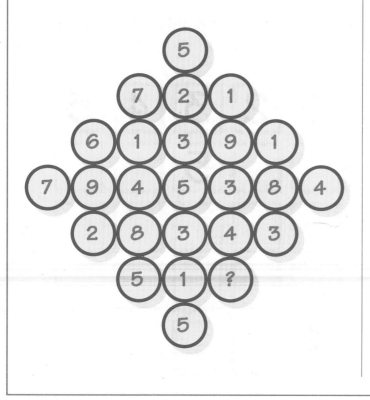

154 Move from the bottom left-hand circle to the top right-hand one adding together all five numbers. Each dark circle is worth minus 5 and so 5 should be taken away from your total each time you meet one. How many different routes giving a total of 10 can be found?

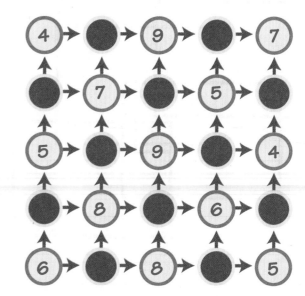

4 Which number should replace the question mark to continue the series?

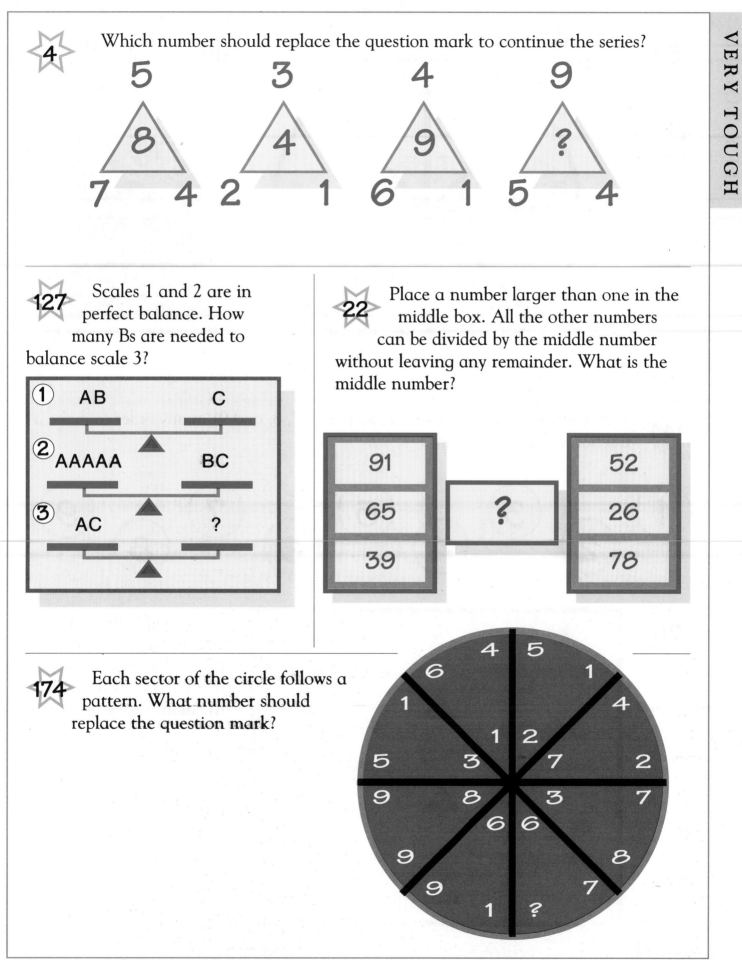

5   3   4   9

8   4   9   ?

7   4   2   1   6   1   5   4

127 Scales 1 and 2 are in perfect balance. How many Bs are needed to balance scale 3?

① AB   C

② AAAAA   BC

③ AC   ?

22 Place a number larger than one in the middle box. All the other numbers can be divided by the middle number without leaving any remainder. What is the middle number?

91
65
39

?

52
26
78

174 Each sector of the circle follows a pattern. What number should replace the question mark?

4   5
6   1
1   4
1   2
5   3   7   2
9   8   3   7
6   6
9   8
9   7
1   ?

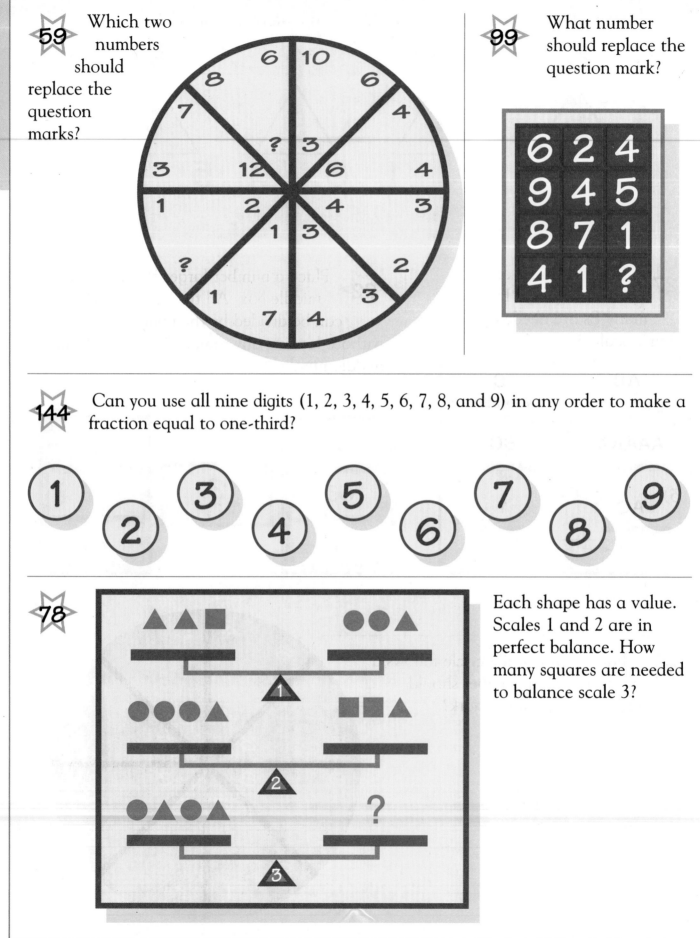

VERY TOUGH

59 Which two numbers should replace the question marks?

99 What number should replace the question mark?

144 Can you use all nine digits (1, 2, 3, 4, 5, 6, 7, 8, and 9) in any order to make a fraction equal to one-third?

78 Each shape has a value. Scales 1 and 2 are in perfect balance. How many squares are needed to balance scale 3?

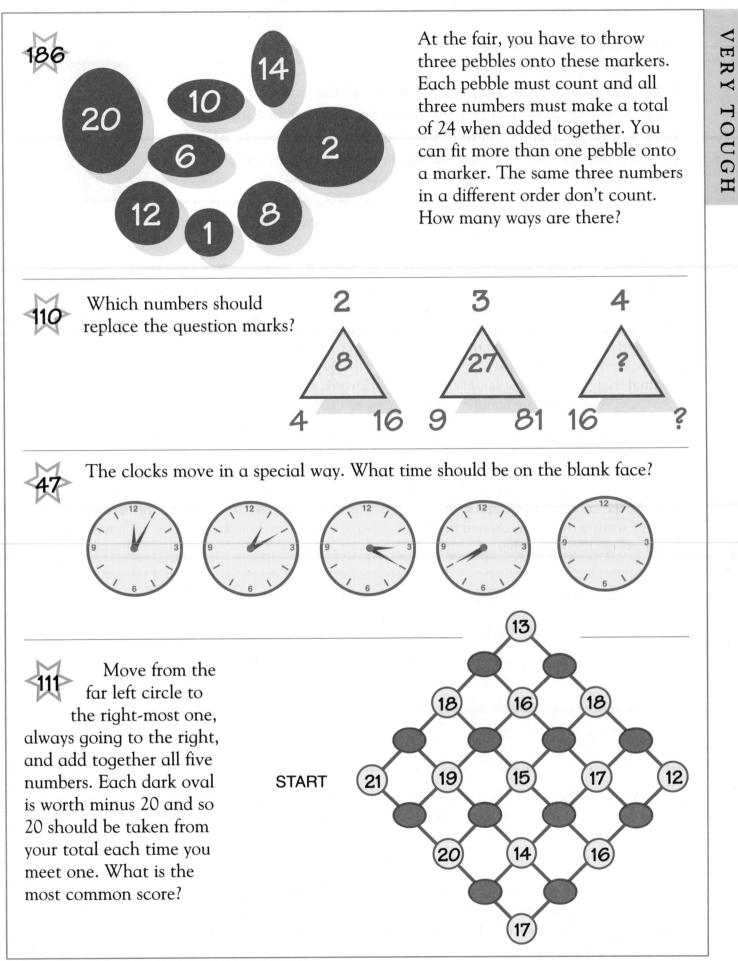

186

At the fair, you have to throw three pebbles onto these markers. Each pebble must count and all three numbers must make a total of 24 when added together. You can fit more than one pebble onto a marker. The same three numbers in a different order don't count. How many ways are there?

110

Which numbers should replace the question marks?

47

The clocks move in a special way. What time should be on the blank face?

111

Move from the far left circle to the right-most one, always going to the right, and add together all five numbers. Each dark oval is worth minus 20 and so 20 should be taken from your total each time you meet one. What is the most common score?

START

An Introduction To Codes

Breaking codes can be very hard. Almost all the codes in this chapter will be taught in this introductory section, but just to keep you on your toes, there are some puzzles where we've given you no clues at all. You'll have to figure them out yourself!

WARNING!
If you would rather try to crack our codes the hard way don't read on, go straight to Page **47**.

Let's try something easy first. There are some forms of disguised writing that are not really codes at all, but they can still be used to convey secret messages.

Simple Codes

If you look at example 1 below, you'll see that each word of the sentence has had its letters rearranged. The message reads: "Each word has its letters mixed up." There are many other simple forms of disguised writing. Another is shown in example 2. The message tells you the technique: "Just change the first letter of each word." Once you have picked up a few tricks like this you can make up all kinds of secret messages. If you take all the vowels out of your message, you get sentences like example 3: "Messages with no vowels look very strange until you get the knack of reading them". Example 4 is one final trick; it is a simple sentence written backwards, and reads: "Writing backwards will fool casual readers". There are hundreds of variations you can try.

One of the simplest codes was invented by the Roman emperor Julius Caesar and is known as Caesar's Letter. Make two lists of the alphabet next to each other, one starting at A, and another starting at B. Then, instead of the letter in the first column, you write the letter in the second column. A becomes B, B becomes C, and so on. Starting at different letters will give you up to 25 codes to use. Example 5 below starts the second column at J, and says: "You can read this with ease." You can use this technique more easily by writing the letters around the edges of two different-sized circles and making a wheel with the letters next to each other.

1	CAHE RWDO SAH TSI TTEERLS XIMDE PU
2	KUST DHANGE YHE BIRST OETTER PF DACH BORD
3	MSSGS WTH N VWLS LK VRY STRNG NTL Y GT TH KNCK F RDNG THM
4	SREDAER LAUSAC LOOF LLIW SDRAWKCAB GNITIRW
5	HXD LJW ANJM CQRB FRCQ NJBN

You can use numbers, too. The easiest numerical code involves giving letters a value based on their position in the alphabet. Using this code A=1, B=2, and so on until you reach Z=26.
14.21.13.2.5.18.19/ 3.1.14/ 5.1.19.9.12.25/ 2.5/ 3.8.1.14.7.5.4/ 9.14.20.15/ 12.5.20.20.5.18.19
This says :"Numbers can easily be changed into letters."

Again, you can work on variations. An obvious one is to number the alphabet backwards. Or you could start in the middle and number the letters from M to A as 1 to 13, and N to Z as 26 to 14. You could give the first half of the alphabet odd numbers (A=1, B=3, C=5, etc) and the second half even ones (N=2, O=4, P=6, etc).

Common Codes

Another type of code that can be a lot of fun is the grid. We have included two variations on this theme. In the first diagram, you will see that the letters have been written into a 5 x 5 grid (I and J share a space). You can now replace the letters by their coordinates. A becomes A1, B becomes A2, and so on. If you wanted to use this code to beat out a message you would use two sets of thumps with a short pause between them.

E2.D2.B4.D4.A5/D3.A5.A3.D2.A5.D4.C1.E4

This says: "Write secretly."

	1	2	3	4	5
A	A	B	C	D	E
B	F	G	H	I J	K
C	L	M	N	O	P
D	Q	R	S	T	U
E	V	W	X	Y	Z

You can also write the letters into the grid in a different order, such as backwards. There are also other ways to complicate the grid. This grid contains nine segments (right), so that each, except the last, contains three letters, and it uses dots to select the letters. A section of grid with no dots means the first letter in that section. One dot means the second letter, and two dots means the third letter.

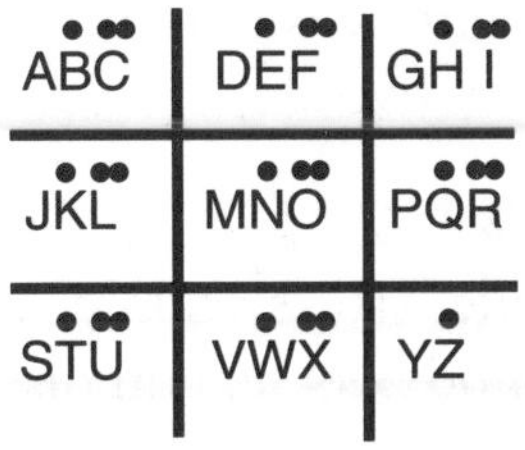

ABC	DEF	GHI
JKL	MNO	PQR
STU	VWX	YZ

This says: "The plot thickens."

A variation of this has just two letters in each segment, (1 or 0 dots), and the last eight letters go inside a four-segment shape like an X, again with 1 or 0 dots. There are many other forms of coded writing that involve substituting symbols for letters. One of the most interesting was a system that used mystic symbols. It was used by alchemists who feared that their secrets would be uncovered by a rival.

A ⊙ B ♃ C ♄ D ♈ E ♆ F ☉ G ♀ H ♂ I ☿ J ☾ K ☼ L Ⅱ M ♋
N ♌ O ♍ P ♎ Q ♏ R ♐ S ♑ T ♒ U ♈ V ♒ W ➤ X X Y Y Z Z

Morse Code

Morse code, invented by Samuel Morse who telegraphed his first message in 1838, has been widely used to transmit secret information. Its system of dots and dashes makes it one of the most adaptable codes in common use. Many organisations still use it today.

A	B	C	D	E	F	G	H	I
J	K	L	M	N	O	P	Q	R
S	T	U	V	W	X	Y	Z	

Morse messages can be sent very rapidly by radio, telegraph, flashing lights, sounds, and many other ingenious methods, using a short tone, click, flash or beep for the dot and a longer one for the dash. The code takes very little time to learn (though transmitting and reading at speed are skills that do take time to acquire).

As with other codes, it is possible to make changes that will fool an outsider who gets hold of your message. For example, you can exchange dots for dashes and vice versa.

The message reads: "Butch Cassidy spotted in Tucson last Monday."

Semaphore

Another very common code is "semaphore," which depends on the sender using flags held at different angles to represent letters. This code has limited use for practical purposes because the sender needs to be in plain view of the recipient. It is mainly used by two ships at sea.

Braille

"Braille," the system of writing devised for blind people, can also be used as an effective code. A system of dots based on a domino layout will allow you to write a message that only initiates will be able to decode. Watch the dots in our puzzles, and not just on dominoes!

This says "This code is Braille".

Other Codes

You can devise symbols of your own to represent letters. Here is a system using differently divided circles.

Message reads: "This code looks mathematical and is great for school."

Finally, here is another code system that was developed for use by the visually impaired. It is called "Moon" writing after its inventor William Moon. Just like Braille it was intended to be embossed on paper so that people could read it by feeling the bumps with their fingertips. Here is a Moon message:

Message reads: "You will be over the moon when you read this."

(165) Bridging The Gap

Walking through treacherous terrain you reach a wide canyon which you must cross. Three rope bridges span the drop; you must decide which one to take. Choose wrongly and you will fall. A sign at each bridge, when decoded, may give you a clue.

1.
2.
3.

(11) Missing Magnus

Newspaper tycoon Magnus Loot couldn't stand the pressure of work. He decided to slip away for a break. He couldn't tell anyone where he was going, or he would be bothered all the time, but he didn't want people to panic. He decided to leave a coded message (below) just difficult enough to keep them guessing while he made his getaway. Can you figure out what Magnus said? The code isn't tricky, just a bit mixed up.

> ONEGO-THUOT-SFOEN-CRAFC-ABKRI-FYAD

(86) Computer Crime

Clive Kilobyte, computer software genius, found that his secrets were being sold to his competitors. But how? He spotted a delivery note due to be sent out. The numbers looked odd – code perhaps? He tried 1=A but got nowhere. Suddenly, a thought struck him, and within minutes he was able to sack the culprit. What was the secret?

19.22/19.26.8/26.13.22.4/11.9.12.20.9.26.14/26.15.14.12.8.7/21.18

13.18.8.19.22.23/18/4.18.15.15/8.22.13.23/2.12.6/23.22.7.26.18.15.8

26.8.26.11/8.26.14

(192) Teacher Torture

Mr. Prim caught Mike passing a note to Clare during a Latin lesson. "What is this all about?" he inquired. "It's a note," replied Mike. "Yes, but it's in some kind of code. What does it say?" Mike said it wasn't code at all. Mr. Prim took a careful look but realized he couldn't unravel the message. Can you?

(132) Candle Kerfuffle

Ms. Agelessia keeps her age secret. Her friends ask you, as an employee of hers, to discover it. Her birthday is soon and they want the right number of candles for her cake. You find her birth certificate, but even the date on that has been covered with a peculiar scrawl. Can you reveal her true date of birth?

(65) Absent Astronaut

During a space mission, an astronaut vanished while moon-walking. Concerned, the other astronauts went to look for their friend. There was no sign of her but in the dust was a coded message. Can you figure out what happened?

B5 B4 A4 C3 A1 C5 C5 A5 A4 /
A2 E4 / D4 B3 A5 /
A5 C3 A5 C2 E4

A1 C2 / C4 C3 / D3 C5 A1 A3
A5 D3 B3 B4 C5 /
A3 A1 C1 C1 A5 A4 / C2 E4 D1
D5 D2 / D4 E2 C4

B3 A5 C1 C5

(80) Pecos Perplexed

Pecos Pete is trying to find a gold mine left to him by his Uncle Josh. However, Josh knew that the location of the mine might be discovered by others. He left directions in code. Can you help Pete crack the code?

(142) Fishy Findings

SQDZRTQD HR

ATQHDC HM BZUD ZS

AZRD NE GHFGRDZ

AZX BKHEER

Wendy Whiting loved diving around old wrecks. One day, while on a dive, she found an old treasure chest buried inside a wreck. The chest was empty, but written on the inside of the lid was what seemed to be a foreign language. Wendy was intrigued so she brought it up to her boat and had a look. Soon she knew the truth and headed straight for shore. What had she discovered?

⑨ Trunk Test

A trunk containing various anonymous long-lost manuscripts is unearthed in the middle of a farmer's field. Literary experts argue for weeks about who the author was, but can't agree. A son of one of the experts wanders over to the trunk and absent-mindedly runs his fingers over the mysterious pattern on the side and cries out, "I know the name of the author!" Do you?

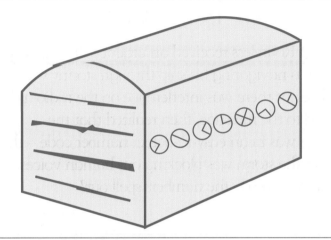

⑫④ Hackers' Horror

On a dark and dismal night, computer hackers break into Computer Craze headquarters in an attempt to find a written copy of the password they have been unable—as yet—to discover. They raid the offices and find a strange pattern imprinted on an imposing piece of cardboard. Realizing its importance, they study it for hours to unlock the mystery of the computer code. What is it?

㉑ Crate Clue

The police raided the Dirty Duck, a bar and hideout for crooks. Their undercover officer seemed to be wrong – the place was empty. All they found were some old beer crates. Then, one officer noticed that some bottle tops had been pierced. What did it mean?

⑰③ Things To Come

Mr. McGuckin labels a box containing test papers in code. It appears just to be an abstract pattern, so as to prevent inquisitive eyes from realizing what the box contains and attempting to find out more. Can you figure out what subject the test is for and when it will be held?

ζ ζγ ζζζ γ ζ

ζγζ

ζζζζ ζζ ζζζ γ

γγγ ζγζ γζγγ

γ ζ ζζζ γ

(52) Et Tu Brute

Brutus and his conspirators want to get rid of Julius Caesar, and have decided to assassinate him. Brutus has written to Cassius giving him details of their murderous plan. Stupidly, he has used Caesar's own code. Caesar's agents have obtained a copy of the message. Can you help them crack the code in time?

FN BQJUU
BCJK QRV RW
CQN OXADV

(91)

122 12 121 21 11 21
221
11 2121 1 2111 1
121 221
1211 222 222 22
11 21 221

Nautical Numbers

Captain Routeless received an urgent radio message as he was navigating his ship through stormy waters. He thought there was interference on the radio as he listened to the message, then realized that the message was in an easy-to-detect number code – the noise of the storm was blocking out human voices. What message do the numbers spell out?

(145) Alien Encounter

Chris is on a space mission to Mars. He is surrounded by a group of three-legged, green aliens. They attempt to converse with him, but when they realize Chris doesn't speak their language, they start to draw strange shapes in the dusty ground. What are they trying to say?

(73) Domino Dilemma

Aliens made contact with Earth. Their message was at first incomprehensible, looking more like a game of dominoes. After a stunning discovery, it was decoded and found to contain a shocking surprise.

(140) A-mazing Message

Becky finds herself trapped in the middle of a huge maze, surrounded by hedges that seem to lead to nowhere. She discovers a pile of pebbles carefully arranged on the ground and stoops down to study the pattern. She realizes it reveals the route to freedom. What must she do?

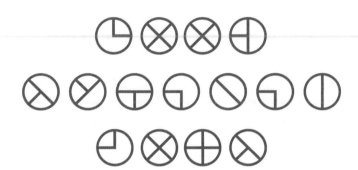

(100) Lost Lyrics

Fading pop star Danny Divine had written a new song that he knew would storm to Number One and save his career. He feared someone would steal his idea. He wrote the lyrics in a special code on the inside of his guitar case. He only got as far as the title when he was called away. When he came back his guitar case was gone! Below is what he had written. Can you decode it?

Tip: there are five vowels and you don't have to stop where you're told to!

2F3.L2.HT.N3.Y1.D1

(46) Time Trouble

A young scientist is trapped in a time machine in a distant century. To activate the time machine, she must decode a password. She's getting desperate to leave but is having trouble finding the password. Can you help her out?

(113) Chalk To The Rescue

Katy is taken hostage by kidnappers. They let her out of a van in a forest while they meet accomplices. She is chained up and can't go far, but gets onto the roof and writes a message with some chalk. The men return, and the journey goes on until a helicopter radios the police. What message made the pilot call?

DIFFICULT

(167) Hidden Treasure

A glossy picture book is published and creates a great stir. It claims to lead the way to a valuable gold casket covered in diamonds. The race is on to decipher the code that leads to the treasure. Can you do it?

(81) Bookham's Blues

You hear something odd in the sound track to your favorite TV cop drama "Bookham"– a bleeping that sounds like Morse code. You jot it down and then try to decode the message.

(12) Dotty Digging

Archeologists were fascinated by some pottery from the Amazonian rain forest. Each piece had the same strange marks hidden on it. What could it mean? No one knew. Then one day, young Dr. Marissa Potts was playing dominoes when she realized. Can you figure it out?

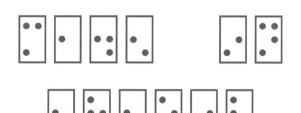

(193) Muddled Matrix

Jeff's dad left the country suddenly, leaving this note for Jeff to follow. He thought it was code but later realized that it wasn't. It plainly gave his father's route! But you have to know where to start.

A	P	O	R	E	U	S
G	H	E	N	S	K	A
N	T	D	A	M	F	R
I	A	R	A	M	R	A
S	T	E	T	S	A	C
K	R	U	F	K	N	H
O	K	G	N	A	B	I

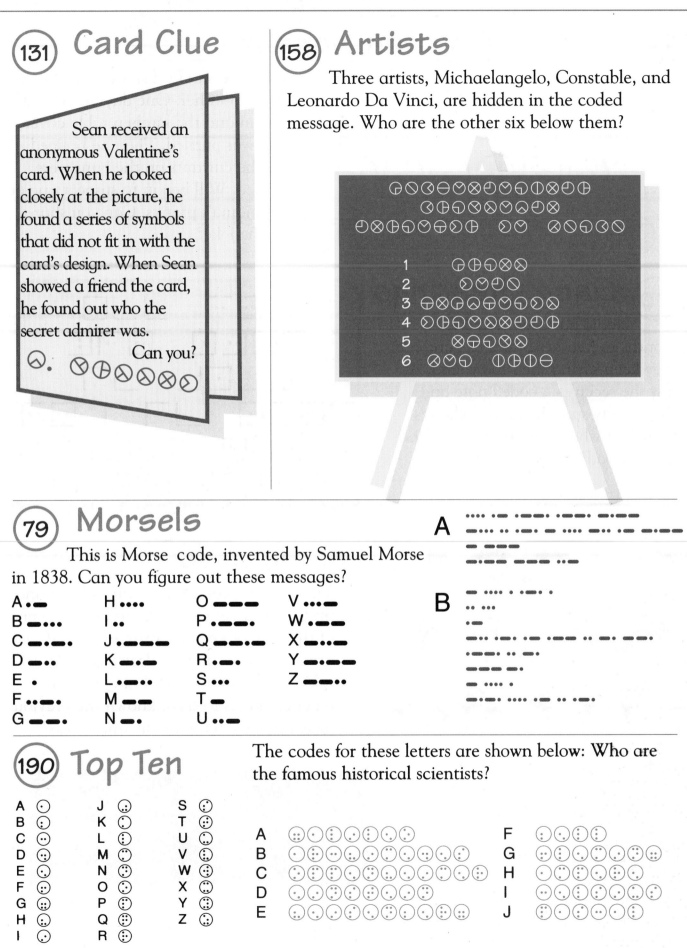

(131) Card Clue

Sean received an anonymous Valentine's card. When he looked closely at the picture, he found a series of symbols that did not fit in with the card's design. When Sean showed a friend the card, he found out who the secret admirer was.

Can you?

(158) Artists

Three artists, Michaelangelo, Constable, and Leonardo Da Vinci, are hidden in the coded message. Who are the other six below them?

(79) Morsels

This is Morse code, invented by Samuel Morse in 1838. Can you figure out these messages?

A .━	H	O ━━━	V ...━
B ━...	I ..	P .━━.	W .━━
C ━.━.	J .━━━	Q ━━.━	X ━..━
D ━..	K ━.━	R .━.	Y ━.━━
E .	L .━..	S ...	Z ━━..
F ..━.	M ━━	T ━	
G ━━.	N ━.	U ..━	

A

B

(190) Top Ten

The codes for these letters are shown below: Who are the famous historical scientists?

A ⊙	J ⸭	S ⸬
B ⸫	K ⊙	T ⸬
C ⊙	L ⊙	U ⊙
D ⊙	M ⊙	V ⸬
E ⊙	N ⊙	W ⸬
F ⊙	O ⊙	X ⸬
G ⸬	P ⸭	Y ⸬
H ⸬	Q ⸭	Z ⸬
I ⊙	R ⸭	

A

B

C

D

E

F

G

H

I

J

126 Bun Bonanza

Will visits his grandma every Friday, and he always gets cakes or buns from her. One day he arrived to find no-one in and the kitchen table covered in buns. He was puzzled. Then he noticed the way the currants on the buns were arranged. Will began to suspect one of Grandma's pranks. Can you share the joke?

30 Gang Greetings

Jodie has been trying for months to join her brother's gang but they keep saying she's too young. At last she receives a coded note and she's pretty sure she knows who it's from. But what does it say? Is it good news or bad? Help her find out.

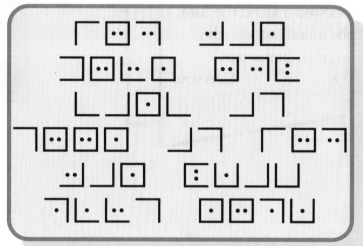

15 Nature's Mysteries

Tim buys a second-hand nature book and opens the cover expecting to see the name of the previous owner. Instead he finds a group of trees carefully drawn out. After taking his book to school one day, the teacher claims to have known the previous owner. Can you figure out who it was?

171 Literary Loot

Detective Cornfield has had a tip-off that a major robbery is going to take place, but he doesn't know when or where. Later, he gets this message. Suddenly, he rushes to the town library! Why? What does the message say?

The arrangements have been booked. Everything you need will be found inside: 38 28 E 22 6 I 8 38 E 24 36 A 16 6 50 4 38 E I 40 I 6 0 46 40 12 0 E 24 A 40 A

(60) Castle Conundrum

Robin Hood has just received a strange message by carrier pigeon. Naturally he and his Merry Men are just itching to dash off on another swashbuckling adventure, but where to? This looks like some sort of grid code, but how does it work?

(97) Initially Puzzling

Even very small changes to a message can help to conceal the meaning. Laura Lane is only six and hasn't been writing for very long but even so she worked out a way of turning a message into code. This is the caption she put on one of her drawings. What did she mean?

Dhis gs hy kog ditting dn fis boghouse gith s vone.

(149) Spread Survey

Shona does a survey to find out if children can identify several different juices. She labels the juices in code to remind herself. No one gets many right. Then one girl correctly names them all, and Shona finds symbols similar to her code on her answer sheet. What does the girl have to say?

(69) Cook's Corner

Sometimes, food needs special preparation in order to be safe. To make sure that no one becomes ill, the company has printed this box of food with important information. Knowing that many of their customers have poor eyesight, special instructions have been included. What needs to be done?

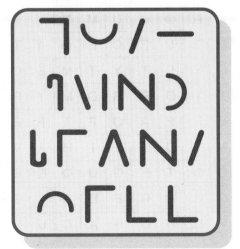

(102) Troublesome Title

Sandra was working on her first novel, but wanted to keep the title a secret until it was complete. She wrote it down in code to prevent herself forgetting it and stop others from seeing it. You have found the code, however, and are intrigued. Can you solve the mystery?

(200) Shipping Shocker

On vacation in Europe, Rita was taking a ferry across the English Channel when she overheard the following message on the captain's radio. Can you explain her shocked expression?

(119) Party Pooper

Alec only wanted really smart kids at his birthday party. He put the invitation in code, and sent it to everyone he knew. His 36 guests had a great time. Could you have gone?

P	A	W	T	C	O	D	A	E	N
Y	R	O	H	U	M	N	Y	V	E
M	T	L	E	O	E	O	A	T	S
O	Y	L	T	Y	T	M	E	C	A
T	I	O	R	R	O	M	Y	P	L
E	F	F	A	O	F	T	F	E	L
M	Y	O	I	L	I	H	A	V	E
O	O	T	H	G	U	O	N	E	T
C	U	A	R	E	B	R	I	G	H
Y	L	N	O	N	A	C	U	O	Y

(128) A Rafty Revelation

A group of teenagers built a raft and set off to sail on the huge lake nearby. After several hours, they realized that they had no idea where their camp was. One of them spotted movement on the shore and told the others. More movement followed with what appeared to be flags, and the route home suddenly became clear. What message did they receive?

(170) Dotty Dave

The *Daily Bugle* held a $200,000 competition. To win you had to find Dotty Dave and call him by name. But how to recognize him? The newspaper said that he could be identified, but did not say how. While on a train, Jennifer suddenly figured it out. She spoke to the man across the aisle, and to the amazement of the other passangers, she won the money. Can you see how she did it?

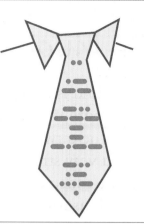

(14) Safe Keeping

Hans Van Helsing is a diamond dealer with a problem. He has forgotten the correct combination for his new super-safe safe. What can he do? It is July 4th and the manufacturers have closed down for the holiday. He can't wait to open the safe.

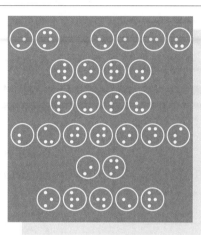

He remembers that he has to press the buttons on the door and that alphabetical order is important. Can you help him break into his own safe?

(194) Cockroach Conundrum

Jim Hill's parents had brought him all the way from L.A. to stay at a real English castle. It was a pain! No clubs, no computer games, and no burgers. He thought he would die. Then he noticed something strange. The castle was full of odd-looking bugs. At first he thought they were some strange English beetles, but when he looked closely, he could see that they were ordinary cockroaches that someone had drawn a delicate pattern on. Take a look at one and see what message the pattern reveals.

(45) Brick Bother

Bill is constructing a top-security building for storing gold, when Ted tries to bribe him for the layout. To avoid getting caught, Bill tells Ted to closely examine a wall he is building for information. Ted agrees and is shocked when he reads Bill's news. What is it?

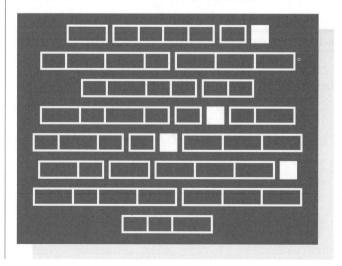

VERY TOUGH

⑧ Much Morsing

Ann Tenna is a radio freak. She spends all her spare time up in her bedroom surfing the airwaves. One day she comes across a very strange transmission. Is this someone's idea of a joke, or is it a national disaster? See what you think.

⑤ Abducted Astronaut

One of NASA's top astronauts has been abducted by foreign agents. FBI agents are handed a scrap of paper that was thrown from the getaway car. It holds a message that appears to be some sort of number substitution code. They try all the obvious codes with no success. Can you solve a mystery that even the FBI cannot?

24.18.10.1.14/13.26.6.18.1/13.3/

11.18.22.9.18.13/

12.10.20.18.3.15.13/10.1/

11.26.1.13.26/2.3.1.10.22.26/4.26

⑱ Dad In Danger

WOOL	EVIL
DOWN	OBOE
SHIN	EYED
BULB	ALLY
DEED	ACTS
KEYS	IBIS

Agent Mike Hero was on a mission of almost unimaginable danger when he received a message saying that he had become a father. Unable to break the habit of a lifetime he asked his superiors to send his wife this message in code.

㉓ Filmstar Frights

Miranda Moneypenny, a famous movie star, was being stalked by an obsessed fan. All her mail was being read and her phone was tapped, so any messages to her had to be written in code. What does this one say?

◇ 1. Digit, Peons, Cacti, Knock, Acorn, Aches, Alias, Bliss, Tread. The answer is deckchair.

◇ 2. Raiders of the Lost Ark.

✹ 3. 20.

✹ 4. 10. The left-hand number is added to the top number and then the right-hand number is subtracted to give the center number.

○ 5. **Abducted Astronaut**

"Being taken to secret hideout in Santa Monica, LA." The alphabet is numbered from the middle. The odd numbers start at N (1) and go to Z (25). The even numbers start at M (2) and go to A (26).

◇ 6. Mike Tyson.

✹ 7. 3. The series reads 1, 2, 3, 1, 2, 3, etc.

○ 8. **Much Morsing**

Have secured television station. Leader will make announcement in one hour.

○ 9. **Trunk Test**

Dickens.

✹ 10. 9.

○ 11. **Missing Magnus**

"Gone to South of France. Back Friday." The dashes are there to mislead.

○ 12. **Dotty Digging**

Made in Brazil.

✹ 13. 2 3 5 7 11 13. These are all prime numbers.

○ 14. **Safe Keeping**

In each word push buttons in order.

○ 15. **Nature's Mysteries**

C. Camore. A large tree is a Morse dash, a small one is a Morse dot.

◇ 16. Blunder, Brigand, Audible, Rebound, Garbled.

◇ 17. California, Idaho, Nebraska, Hawaii, Alaska.

○ 18. **Dad In Danger**

"Well done send baby dad's kiss." The first and last letters of words in the left-hand column form the first and third letters of the new words. The first and last letters of words in the right-hand column form the second and fourth letters of the new words.

◇ 19. Idaho. (London, Paris, Rome, Dallas, Tokyo)

✹ 20. 8. Triangle is worth 2, circle 5 and star 1.

○ 21. **Crate Clue**

"They suspected trouble and ran. Will report again ASAP." The code is Braille.

✹ 22. 13.

○ 23. **Filmstar Frights**

Do not worry. Police have put their plan into action and the culprit is about to be caught.

✹ 24. 14. Diamond 6, Heart 4, Club 3.

✹ 25. 3. The number is found in 3 squares.

◇ 26. Barbados.

◇ 27. When flipped vertically they remain the same.

◇ 28. 1. Alice in Wonderland, 2. Tom Sawyer, 3. Dracula, 4. Gulliver's Travels, 5. The Witches.

✹ 29. 3. The number is in 3 different boxes.

○ 30. **Gang Greetings**

You can join our gang as soon as you can read this note.

✹ 31. 4. The total of each horizontal line doubles from the outside to the center.

✹ 32. 1R.

✹ 33. 27 each of 2V, 5V, 10V, 20V and 50V coins.

◇ 34. Tom Cruise.

✹ 35. 4.

◇ 36. Tyrannosaurus Rex.

◇ 37. $7.80. A=1, B=2, C=3, etc.

◇ 38. Primrose, Buttercup, Daisy, Bluebell, Heather.

◇ 39. Neigh, Snowy, Ready, Thorn, Large.

◇ 40. A.

◇ 41.

P¹	G²	Y³	R⁴	H⁵	T⁶	A⁷	W⁸	I⁹	N¹⁰	E¹¹	V¹²	K¹³
Q¹⁴	U¹⁵	O¹⁶	B¹⁷	Z¹⁸	J¹⁹	D²⁰	M²¹	C²²	X²³	L²⁴	S²⁵	F²⁶

✹ 42. 30.

✹ 43. 1C on the far left.

◇ 44. Bob, Bobs, Bosh, Bole, Boles, Boil, Boils, Bog, Bogs, Bogie, Bogies, Blob, Blobs, Beg, Begs, Bib, Bibs, Bible, Bibles, Bile, Bilge, Big, Oblige, *Obliges*, Oil, Oils, Ogle, Ogles, Ohs, Sob, Sol, Sole, Soli, Soil, Slob,

Sloe, Slog, Sleigh, Silo, Sigh, Shoe, She, Lob, *Lobbies*, Lobs, Lobe, Lobes, Lose, Log, Logs, Loge, Loges, Lei, Leis, Leg, Legs, Lie, Lies, Ebb, Ebbs, Ego, Egos, Isle, Gob, Gobs, Gobble, *Gobbles*, Goes, Glob, Globs, Globe, Globes, Glib, Gel, Gels, Gib, Gibs, Gibe, Gibes, Hob, Hobble, *Hobbles*, *Hobbies*, Hobs, Hose, Hole, Holes, Holies, Hoe, Hoes, Hog, Hogs, His, Hie, Hies.

45. Brick Bother

"The police are onto you." A long brick is a Morse dash, a short one a Morse dot.

46. Time Trouble

Action stations.

47. 4:20. The times move forward by 1 hour and 5 minutes, 2 hours and 10 minutes, 4 hours and 20 minutes, and 8 hours and 40 minutes.

48. Italy, Napoleon, Douglas, Indigo, Apple, Nightmare, Algebra, Jerusalem, Ostrich, Neptune, Emperor, Salami.
The character is Indiana Jones.

49. 17.

50. Swimming, Archery, Football, Athletics, Riding, Ice skating.
The word is Safari.

51. B. It has two faces the same.

52. Et Tu Brute?

"We shall stab him in the Forum." This is a simple letter substitution code: J = A, I = Z, etc.

53. 3 diamonds.

54. 380. The distance is the position of the first letter of the alphabet doubled and multiplied by ten.

55. Medium, Coiled, Academic, Divided, Clouded

56.

57. 3.

58. 47.

59. Outer 3, inner 9. When the numbers in the outer sectors are added together, the sums of the top half are double those of the diagonally opposite bottom halves. For the inner sectors, the numbers in the top half of the circle are three times those of the diagonally opposite bottom ones.

60. Castle Conundrum

"Held captive by wicked uncle. Can you get me out?" The message is from Maid Marian.

61. 7.

62. 4.

63. 55.

64. Square 1E in row 2, column 2.

65. Absent Astronaut

"Kidnapped by the enemy. Am on spaceship called Myqur Two. Help!"
Each number and letter refer to a simple grid code where A1 to A5 represent A to E, B1 to B5 represent F to K, and so on.

66. 8.

67. Little Red Riding Hood.

68. S. (The first letter of Monday, Tuesday, etc.)

69. Cook's Corner

Must grind beans well.

◆ **70.**

Diagram labels: CROWN, TEMPLE, NAPE, BRIDGE, IRIS, LOBE, PALM, ARCH

✹ **71.** 1 3 5 7 9 11. The numbers increase by 2 each time.

✹ **72.** E.

○ **73.** Domino Dilemma

I don't suppose any of you chaps speak English, do you?

✹ **74.** 8 in the outer section at the top, 3 in the outer section below and 5 in the inner one.

◆ **75.** Hockey, Karate, and Tennis.

◆ **76.** Creep, Alibi, Nails, Comic, Eagle, Rails. The signs of the zodiac are Cancer and Pisces.

◆ **77.** The numbers above the line are all three-letter words.

✹ **78.** 2 squares.

○ **79.** Morsels

A. Happy birthday to you.

B. There is a drawing pin on the chair.

○ **80.** Pecos Perplexed

From Dead Men's Gulch ride two hours north until you see a cactus shaped like a letter Y. The mine is one hundred paces east of there.

○ **81.** Bookham's Blues

"Thought you'd never wake up. The murderer is the old lady in the red hat."

◆ **82.** Tiger Woods.

◆ **83.** Knuckles, Duckling, Inklings, Pickling, Includes.

✹ **84.** 7.

✹ **85.** 1. The pattern is symmetrical.

○ **86.** Computer Crime

"He has a new program almost finished I will send you details ASAP - Sam."
This code is backward (26=A, 1=Z).

✹ **87.** 4. The number is found in four overlapping shapes.

◆ **88.** Noiseless Lionesses.

✹ **89.** 3.

✹ **90.** 8. The sequence is even numbers.

○ **91.** Nautical Numbers

Warning – iceberg looming. 1 is a Morse dot, 2 is a Morse dash.

◆ **92.** Catapult. (All the words include the name of an animal).

✹ **93.** 6. C is 2 Bs, and B is 2 As.

✹ **94.** 10. The numbers in each sector are added together and the diagonally opposite sectors have the same total.

◆ **95.** 1. P 2. BAT 3. CURED 4. FANTASY.

✹ **96.** Plus (+) and minus (–).

○ **97.** Initially Puzzling

The first letter of each word is replaced with a random letter. The message reads: "This is my dog sitting in his doghouse with a bone."

◆ **98.** Acrobatic.

✹ **99.** 3. In each row, subtract the middle number from the left to give the right.

○ **100.** Lost Lyrics

"A Day in the Life" (sorry Danny, it's been done!). The words are spelled backward and with numbers in place of the vowels. The periods are there to fool you.

◆ **101.** Ascend, Battle, Arabia, Cheery, Bronze, Eagles, Arctic, Boughs.
The answer is Strength.

○ **102.** Troublesome Title

Red Alert.

◆ **103.** A B H I.

✹ **104.** E.

✹ **105.** 7. It is the only odd number.

✹ **106.** 2. A 2 and its mirror image are placed together top and bottom.

◆ **107.** George Bush, Charles Dickens, Demi Moore, Whitney Houston, Isaac Newton.

ANSWERS

◇ **108.** "If you think this is going to be easy, you had better think again." All the vowels have been removed.

◇ **109.** Fast, Area, Sets, Task.

✴ **110.** Bottom=64, middle=256. The left and top numbers are multiplied and the answer is put in the middle. The top and middle numbers are then multiplied and this answer goes to the right.

✴ **111.** 4 (26 ways).

✴ **112.** 16 is the lowest and there are 2 routes.

◯ **113.** Chalk To The Rescue

SOS stop this van!

◇ **114.** 1. Mar, Ram, Arm. 2. Art, Tar, Rat. 3. Spar, Pars, Raps, Rasp. 4. Miles, Slime, Smile, Limes.

◇ **115.** 32.

✴ **116.** 13.

◇ **117.** 1. Attention, 2. Nitrogen, 3. Nugget, 4. Tolerable, 5. Eerie, 6. Eggplant, 7. Tortoise, 8. Eyewitness, 9. Squabble, 10. Elocution, 11. Nothing.

◇ **118.** *Across*

1. Mast 6. Orphan 8. Pa 9. Rear 10. Ruler 12. Drinks 13. Do 14. Hill 16. Stag 18. Gel 19. Foal 21. Door 23. Corridor.

Down

1. Morning 2. Are 3. Spark 4. Thrush 5. Bandit 7. Needle 11. Roller 15. Igloo 16. Sap 17. Also 19. Far 20. Add 22. Or.

◯ **119.** Party Pooper

"You can only come to my party if you are bright enough to follow the trail I have left for you. Come to my place Monday at seven." Just follow the trail from the bottom right corner.

✴ **120.** 4.

◇ **121.** Rumplestiltskin.

◇ **122.** F, M, N. (Initial letters of the months, with three months together across each large box).

◇ **123.** No. The words in the box begin with one of the vowels in their usual order.

◯ **124.** Hacker's Horror

Systems go.

✴ **125.** 2D, in the fourth column.

◯ **126.** Bun Bonanza

I am hiding upstairs.

✴ **127.** 2.

◯ **128.** A Rafty Revelation

It's behind you!

✴ **129.**

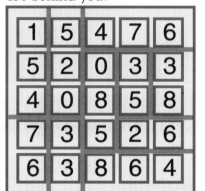

✴ **130.** 8. The numbers down the sides are placed together in the middle section.

◯ **131.** Card Clue

B. Sotted.

◯ **132.** Candle Kerfuffle

April First, Nineteen fifty-five.

◇ **133.** Bugs (all curved letters - no straight lines).

◇ **134.**

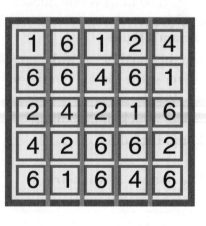

✴ **135.**

136. 4. A times B divided by C gives D.

137. E. (The second letter of January, February, March etc.)

138. One button, square root.($\sqrt{}$)

139. Consonants are worth 4, vowels 2, therefore Washington, DC, is 42 miles away.

140. **A-mazing Message**
Keep turning left.

141. 18.

142. **Fishy Findings**
"Treasure is buried in cave at base of Highsea Bay cliffs." Letters are replaced by the one before in the alphabet.

143. Sea of Tranquility.

144. $\dfrac{5832}{17496} = \dfrac{1}{3}$

145. **Alien Encounter**
Like a cup of tea?

146. 6:00 am.

147. 4A and 4D are the same.

148. 3. Each slice adds up to 3.

149. **Spread Survey**
I know this too!

150. 14.

151. Fridge, Oven, Microwave, Kettle, Saucer.

152. Barter, Balloon, Create, Trader, Looter, Berate.

153. 19.

154. 5.

155. 1E, 4C, and 5A.

156. Nurse, Pilot, Teacher, Accountant, Disc jockey.

157. T. (The first letter of one, two, three etc.)

158. **Artists**
1. Monet, 2. Dali, 3. Rembrandt, 4. Donatello, 5. Ernst, 6. Van Gogh.

159. 22. Star is worth 10, triangle is worth 8, circle is worth 3 and square is worth 1.

160. Beethoven.

161.

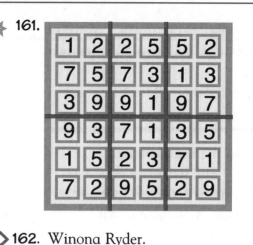

162. Winona Ryder.

163. 25.

164. 6. Column D is the total of A+B+C.

165. **Bridging The Gap**
1. Deadly drop, 2. Safe and Secure, 3. Plummet point. (Bridge number 2 is therefore the bridge to take.)

166. Robinson Crusoe, Swiss Family Robinson, The Three Musketeers, Lord of the Rings, Huckleberry Finn.

167. **Hidden Treasure**
The oak tree, Luckyhull.

168. 2C, 3B, and 4A.

169. 2, 4, 6, 8, 10, 12. The numbers increase by 2 each time.

170. **Dotty Dave**
I am Dotty Dave.

171. **Literary Loot**
The book to look in is *A Tale of Two Cities* by Charles Dickens. The numbers give a message written backward, with the vowels uncoded, but the consonants are represented by a number that is double their alphabetic value.

172. 4 and 1 – add the top line to the bottom line to give the middle line.

173. **Things To Come**
Easter history test. ζ is a Morse dash, γ is a Morse dot.

174. 9. Each sector in the bottom half of the circle totals double its opposite.

175. 3.

176. Glockenspiel.

177. 2. A is 2xB, so 4xB is 2xA.

ANSWERS

◇**178.** Consonants are worth 7, vowels 8. Therefore Beijing is 52 miles away.

✳**179.** 6.

◇**180.** Butter, Totter, Barrel, Longer, Rubble, Totals.

◇**181.** E.

✳**182.** 2D in the third column.

✳**183.** 7. A 7 and its mirror image are together.

◇**184.** 1. London 2. Onion 3. Once
4. Cease 5. Several 6. Allow
7. Owner 8. Erase 9. Senior
10. Order 11. Era 12. Astronomy
13. Myrrh 14. Rhyme
15. Medicine 16. Nervous
17. Usual 18. Aladdin
19. Invisible 20. Lemon 21. One
22. Newer 23. Eradicate
24. Terror 25. Orchards

◇**185.** Earwig, Centipede, Tarantula, Cockroach, Earthworm.

✳**186.** 6 ways.

✳**187.** Each pair of numbers on each row total 20. The first two on the bottom row, 2 and 10, do not.

◇**188.** Tail, Nostril, Lair, Just. The 10 letter word is journalist.

◇**189.** Mother Goose.

○**190.** **Top Ten**
A. Galileo B. Archimedes
C. Oppenheimer D. Einstein
E. Heisenberg F. Bell G. Fleming
H. Ampere I. Celsius J. Pascal.

✳**191.** 16.

○**192.** **Teacher Torture**
"I hate Latin. Let's meet after school and go for a burger and cola." Start with the I at the top right.

○**193.** **Muddled Matrix**
"Amsterdam, Frankfurt, Athens, Karachi, Bangkok, Singapore, US." Start at the A in the exact middle and go in a clockwise direction.

○**194.** **Cockroach Conundrum**
Prisoner in dungeons. Help.

◇**195.** Bart Simpson and Aladdin.

◇**196.** Joust, Joist, Joint, Point, Paint, Pains. Clock, Cloak, Croak, Creak, Break, Bread.

◇**197.**

✳**198.**

7	3	3	7
6	4	6	4
3	6	3	7
4	7	6	4

✳**199.** 4.

○**200.** **Shipping Shocker**
SOS, SOS. This is Royal Yacht Britannia. Sinking fast. God save the Queen.